A VARIETY O

Books by Max Beerbohm

A VARIETY OF THINGS

BY

MAX BEERBOHM

WILLIAM HEINEMANN LTD
MELBOURNE :: LONDON :: TORONTO

FIRST PUBLISHED 1928
THIS EDITION 1953

PRINTED IN GREAT BRITAIN
AT THE WINDMILL PRESS
KINGSWOOD, SURREY

CONTENTS

CONTENTS

NOTE

" A Variety of Things " was published in 1928 as one of the volumes in a limited edition of my writings. (From the present edition one item, " The Happy Hypocrite " is omitted.)

I should mention that " The Guerdon " was written when Henry James was given the Order of Merit, and that " The Dreadful Dragon of Hay Hill " was conceived in the course of the 1914–1918 war, and that " A Social Success " was produced in 1913 by George Alexander.

M. B.
1953.

THE DREADFUL DRAGON
OF HAY HILL

THE DREADFUL DRAGON
OF HAY HILL

I

In the faint early dawn of a day in the midst of a golden
summer, a column of smoke was seen rising from Hay
Hill, rising thickly, not without sparks in it. Danger to
the lives of the dressmakers in Dover Street was not appre-
hended. The fire-brigade was not called out. The fire-
brigade had not been called into existence. Dover Street
had not yet been built. I tell of a time that was thirty-nine
thousand years before the birth of Christ.

To imagine Hay Hill as it then was, you must forget
much of what, as you approach it from Berkeley Square or
from Piccadilly, it is now. You knew it in better days, as
I did?—days when its seemly old Georgian charm had
not vanished under the superimposition of two vast high
barracks for the wealthier sort of bachelors to live in?
You remember how, in frosty weather, the horse of your
hansom used to skate hopelessly down the slope of it and
collapse, pitching you out, at the foot of it? Such memories
will not serve. They are far too recent. You must imagine
just a green hill, with some trees and bushes on it. You
must imagine it far higher than it is nowadays, tapering
to a summit not yet planed off for the purpose of Dover
Street; and steeper; and with two caves aloft in it; and
bright, bright green.

And conceive that its smiling wildness made no contrast
with aught that was around. Berkeley Square smiled wildly

3

too. Berkeley Square had no squareness. It was but a green valley that went, uninterrupted by any Piccadilly, into the Green Park. And through the midst of it a clear stream went babbling and meandering, making all manner of queer twists and turns on its off-hand way to the marsh-lands of Pimlico down yonder. Modern engineers have driven this stream ignominiously underground; but at that time there it still was, visible, playful, fringed by reeds, darted about in by small fishes, licensed to reflect sky. And it had tributaries! The landscape that I speak of, the great rolling landscape that comprised all Mayfair, was everywhere intersected by tiny brooks, whose waters, for what they were worth, sooner or later trickled brightly into that main stream. Here and there, quite fortuitously, in groups or singly, stood willows and silver birches, full of that wistful grace which we regard as peculiarly modern. But not till the landscape reached Hyde Park did trees exert a strong influence over it. Then they exerted a very strong influence indeed. They hemmed the whole thing in. Hyde Park, which was a dense and immemorial forest, did not pause where the Marble Arch is, but swept on to envelop all Paddington and Marylebone and most of Bloomsbury, and then, skirting Soho, over-ran everything from Covent Garden to Fetter Lane, and in a rush south-ward was brought up sharp only by the edge of the sheer cliffs that banked this part of the Thames.

The Thames, wherever it was not thus sharply opposed, was as tyrannous as the very forest. It knew no mercy for the lowly. Westminster, like Pimlico, was a mere swamp, miasmal, malarial, frequented by frogs only, whose croaks, no other sound intervening, made hideous to the ear a district now nobly and forever resonant with the silver voices of choristers and the golden voices of senators. Westminster is firm underfoot nowadays ; yet, even so, as you come away from it up the Duke of York's steps, you feel that you are mounting into a drier, brisker air ; and this sensation is powerfully repeated when anon you climb St. James's Street. Not lower, you feel, not lower than Piccadilly would you have your home. And this, it would seem, was just what the average man felt forty-one thousand years ago. Nature had placed in the steep chalky slopes from the marshes a fair number of commodious caves ; but these were almost always vacant. Only on the higher levels did human creatures abound.

And scant enough, by our present standards, that abundance was. In all the space which the forest had left free—not merely all Mayfair, remember : all Soho, too, and all that lies between them—the population was hardly more than three hundred souls. So low a figure is hard to grasp. So few people, in a place so teeming now, are almost beneath our notice. Almost, but not quite. What there was of them was not bad.

Nature, as a Roman truly said, does not work by leaps. What we call Evolution is a quite exasperatingly slow process. We should like to compare favourably with even the latest of our predecessors. We wince whenever we read a declaration by some eminent biologist that the skull of the prehistoric man whose bones have just been un-earthed in this or that district differs but slightly from the skull of the average man in the twentieth century. I hate having to tell you that the persons in this narrative had well-shaped heads, and that if their jaws were more prominent, their teeth sharper, their backs less upright, their arms longer and hairier, and their feet suppler than our own, the difference in each case was so faint as to be almost negligible.

Of course they were a simpler folk than we are. They knew far less than we know. They did not, for example, know they were living thirty-nine thousand years before Christ ; and ' protopalaeolithic ' was a term they *never* used. They regarded themselves as very modern and very greatly enlightened. They marvelled at their ingenuities in the use of flint and stone. They held that their ancestors had been crude in thought and in mode of life, but not unblest with a certain vigour and nobility of character which they themselves lacked. They thought that their descendants would be a rather feeble, peevish race, yet that somehow, in the far future a state of general goodness and felicity would set in, to abide forever. But I seem to be failing in my effort to stress the difference between these people and ourselves. Let us hold fast to the pleasing fact that they really were less well-educated.

They could neither read nor write, and were so weak in their arithmetic that not a shepherd among them could count his sheep correctly, nor a goat-herd his goats. And their pitiful geography ! Glancing northward above their forest, they saw the mountainous gaunt region that is Hampstead, that is Highgate ; southward, across the river and its wide fens, the ridges of a nameless Surrey ; but as to how the land lay beyond those barriers they had only the haziest notion. That there was land they knew. For, though they themselves never ventured further than the edge of the marshes, or than the fringe of the tangled forest that bounded the rest of their domain, certain other people were more venturesome : often enough it would happen that some stranger, some dark-haired and dark-eyed nomad, passed this way, blinking from the forest or soaked from the river; and glad always was such an one to rest awhile here, and tell to his good hosts tales of the outlying world. Tales very marvellous to the dwellers in this sleek safe homeland!—tales of rugged places where no men are, or few, and these in peril by night and by day; tales of the lion, a creature with yellow eyes and a great mop of yellow hair to his head, a swift and strong creature, without pity; and of the tusked mastodon, taller than the oldest oak, and shaking the ground he walks on; and of the winged dragon, that huge beast, poising so high in the air that he looks no bigger than a hawk, yet reaching his prey on earth as instantly as a hawk his; and of the huge crawling dragon, that breathes fire through his nostrils and scorches black the grass as he goes hunting, hunting; of the elephant, who fears nothing but mastodons and dragons; of the hyena and the tiger, and of beasts beside whom these seem not dreadful.

Wide-eyed, open-mouthed, the homelanders would sit listening. 'O wanderer,' would say one, 'tell us more of the mastodon, that is taller than the oldest oak.' And another would say, 'Make again for us, O wanderer, the noise that a lion makes.' And another, 'Tell us more of the dragon that scorches black the grass as he goes hunting, hunting.' And another, 'O you that have so much wandered, surely you will abide here always? Here is not hardship nor danger. We go not in fear of the beasts whose roast flesh you have tasted and have praised. Rather go they in great fear of us. The savoury deer flees from us, and has swifter feet than we have, yet escapes not the point of the thrown spear, and falls, and is ours. The hare is not often luckier, such is our skill. Our goats and our sheep would flee from us, but dare not, fearing the teeth of certain dogs who love us. We slay what we will for food. For us all there is plenty in all seasons. You have drunk of the water of our stream. Is it not fresh and cold? Have you cracked in your wanderings better nuts than ours? or bitten juicier apples? Surely you will abide here always.'

And to the wanderer it would seem no bad thing that he should do so. Yet he did not so. When the sun had sunk and risen a few times he would stretch his arms, maybe gazing round at the landscape with a rather sardonic smile, and be gone through the forest or across the water. And the homelanders, nettled, would shrug their shoulders, and thank their gods for having rid them of a fool.

Their gods were many, including the sun and moon, their clear stream, apple-trees and cherry-trees and fig-trees and trees that gave nuts, rose-bushes in summer, rain, and also fire—fire, the god that themselves had learnt to make from flint, fire that made meat itself godlike. But they prayed to no god, not being aware that they needed anything. And they had no priesthood. When a youth lost his heart to a maid he approached her, and laid his hands gently upon her shoulders, and then, if she did not turn away from him, he put his hands about her waist and lifted her three times from the ground. This sufficed: they were now man and wife, and lived happily, or not so, ever after. Nor was it needful that the rite should be only thus. If a maid lost her heart to a youth, the laid hands could be hers, and the shoulders his, and if he turned not away from her, if thrice he lifted her from the ground, this too was wedlock.

If there were no good cave for them to take as their own, bride and bridegroom built them a hut of clay and wattles. Such huts were already numerous, dotted about in all directions. Elder folk thought them very ugly, and said that they spoilt the landscape. Yet what was to be done? It is well that a people should multiply. Though these homelanders now deemed themselves very many indeed (their number, you see, being so much higher than they ever could count up to, even incorrectly), yet not even the eldest of them denied that there was plenty of room and plenty of food for more. And plenty of employment, you ask? They did not worry about that. The more babies there were, the more children and grown folk would there be anon to take turns in minding the ample flocks and herds, and the more leisure for all to walk or sit around, talking about the weather or about one another. They made no fetish of employment.

I have said that they were not bad. Had you heard them talked about by one another, you might rather doubt this estimate. You would have heard little good of any one. No family seemed to approve of its neighbours. Even between brothers and sisters mutual trust was rare. Even husbands and wives bickered. To strangers, as you have seen, these people could be charming. I do not say they were ever violent among themselves. That was not their way. But they lacked kindness.

Happiness is said to beget kindness. Were these people not happy? They deemed themselves so. Nay, there was to come a time when, looking back, they felt that they had been marvellously happy. This time began on the day in whose dawn smoke was seen rising from Hay Hill.

The title of my tale has enabled you to guess the source of that smoke : the nostrils of some dreadful dragon. But had you been the little girl named Thia, by whom first that smoke was seen, you would not have come upon the truth so quickly.

Thia had slept out under the stars, and, waking as they faded, had risen, brushed the dew from her arms and legs, shaken it off her little goatskin tunic, and gone with no glance around or upward to look for mushrooms. Presently, as there seemed to be no mushrooms this morning anywhere, she let her eyes rove from the ground (ground that is now Lord Lansdowne's courtyard) and, looking up, saw the thick smoke above the hill. She saw that it came from the cave where dwelt the widow Gra with her four children. How could Gra, how could any one, want a fire just now ? Thia's dark eyes filled with wonder. On wintry nights it was proper that there should be a fire at the mouth of every cave, proper that in wintry dawns these should still be smouldering. But—such smoke as this on such a morning ! Heavier, thicker smoke than Thia had ever seen in all the ten years of her existence ! Of course fire was a god. But surely he would not have us worship him to-day? Why then had Gra lit him ? Thia gave it up, and moved away with eyes downcast in renewed hope of mushrooms.

She had not gone far before she stared back again, hearing a piteous shrill scream from the hill. She saw a little boy flying headlong down the slope—Thol, the little red-haired boy who lived in the other cave up there. Thol slipped, tumbled head over heels, rolled, picked himself up, saw Thia, and rushed weeping towards her.

'What ails you, O child?' asked Thia, than whom Thol was indeed a year younger and much smaller.

'O!' was all that the child vouchsafed between his sobs, 'O!'

Thia thought ill of tears. Scorn for Thol fought the maternal instinct in her. But scorn had the worst of it. She put her arms about Thol. Quaveringly he told her what he had just seen, and what he believed it to be, and how it lay there asleep, with just its head and tail outside Gra's cave, snoring. Then he broke down utterly. Thia looked at the hill. Maternal instinct was now worsted by wonder and curiosity and the desire to be very brave—to show how much braver than boys girls are. Thia went to the hill, shaking off Thol's wild clutches and leaving him behind. Thia went up the hill, quickly but warily, on tiptoe, wide-eyed, with her tongue out upon her underlip. She took a sidelong course, and she noticed a sort of black path through the grass, winding from the mouth of Gra's cave, down one side of the hill, and away, away till it was lost in the white mists over the marshes. She climbed nearly level with the cave's mouth, and then, peering through a bush which hid her, saw what lay behind the veil of smoke.

Much worse the sleeping thing was than she had feared it would be, much huger and more hideous. Its face was as long as a man's body, and lay flat out along the ground. Had Thia ever seen a crocodile's face, that is of what she would have been reminded—a crocodile, but with great pricked-up ears, and snuffling forth fiery murk in deep, rhythmic, luxurious exhalations. The tip of the creature's tail, sticking out from the further side of the cave's mouth, looked to her very like an arrow-head of flint—green flint ! She could awfully imagine the rest of the beast, curled around in the wide deep cave. And she shuddered with a great hatred, and tears started to her eyes, as she thought of Gra and of those others.

When she reached the valley, it was clear to Thol that she had been crying. And she, resenting his scrutiny, made haste to say, ' I wept for Gra and for her children ; but you, O child, because you are a coward.'

At these words the boy made within him a great resolve. This was, that he would slay the dragon.

III

How ? He had not thought of that. When ? Not to-day, he felt, nor to-morrow. But some day, somehow. He knew himself to be small, even for his age, and the dragon big for whatever its age might be. He knew he was not very clever ; he was sure the dragon was very clever indeed. So he said nothing to Thia of his great resolve that she should be sorry.

Meanwhile, the sun had risen over the hills beyond the water, and the birds been interrupted in their songs by the bleating of penned sheep. This sound recalled Thol from his dreams of future glory.

For he was a shepherd's lad. It was the custom that children, as they ceased to toddle, should begin to join in whatever work their parents were by way of doing for the common good. Indeed it was felt that work was especially a thing for the young. Thol had no parents to help ; for his mother had died in giving him birth ; and one day, when he was but seven years old, his father, who was a shepherd, had been attacked and killed by an angry ram. In the sleek safe homeland this death by violence had made a very painful impression. There was a general desire to hush it up, to forget it. Thol was a reminder of it. Thol was ignored, as much as possible. He was allowed to have the cave that had been his father's, but even the widow Gra, in the cave so near to his, disregarded him, and forbade her children to play with him. However, there dwelt hard by in the valley a certain shepherd, named Brud, and he, being childless, saw use for Thol as helping-boy, and to that use put him. Every morning, it was Thol's first duty to wake his master. It was easy for Thol himself to wake early, for his cave faced eastwards. To-day in his great excitement about the dragon he had forgotten his duty to Brud. He went running now to perform it.

Brud and his dog, awakened, came out and listened to Thol's tale. Truthfulness was regarded by all the home-landers as a very important thing, especially for the young. Brud took his staff, and ' Now, O Thol,' he said, ' will I beat you for saying the thing that is not.' But the boy protested that there was indeed a dragon in Gra's cave ; so Brud said sagely, ' Choose then one of two things : either to run hence into Gra's cave, or to be beaten.' Thol so unhesitatingly chose to be beaten that it was clear he did believe his own story. Thia, moreover, came running up to say that there truly was a dragon. So Brud did not beat Thol very much, and went away with his dog towards the hill, curious to know what really was amiss up there.

Perhaps Thia was already sorry she had called Thol a coward, for, though he was now crying again loudly, she did but try to comfort him. His response to her effort was not worthy of a future hero : he complained through his tears that she had not been beaten, too, for saying there was a dragon. Thia's eyes flashed fiercely. She told Thol he was ugly and puny and freckle-faced, and that nobody loved him. All this was true, and it came with the more crushing force from pretty Thia, whom every one petted.

No one ever made Thia work, though she was strong and agile, and did wondrously well whatever task she might do for the fun of it. She could milk a goat, or light a fire, or drive a flock of geese, or find mushrooms if there were any, as quickly and surely as though she had practised hard for years. But the homelanders preferred to see her go flitting freely all the day long, dancing and carolling, with flowers in her hair.

Thia's hair was as dark as her eyes. Thia was no daughter of the homeland. She was the daughter of two wanderers who, seven years ago, had sojourned here for a few days. Their child had then attained just that age which was always a crisis in the lives of wanderers' children : she had grown enough to be heavy in her parents' arms, and not enough to foot it beside them. So they had left her here, promising the homelanders that in time they would come back for her ; and she, who had had no home, had one now. Although (a relic, this, of primitive days) no homelander ever on any account went near to the mouth of another's dwelling, Thia would go near and go in, and be always welcome. The homelanders seldom praised one another's children ; but about Thia there was no cause for jealousy : they all praised her strange beauty, her fearless and bright ways. And withal she was very good. You must not blame her for lack of filial sense. How should she love parents whom she did not remember? She was full of love for the homelanders; and naturally she hated the thought they hated: that some day two wanderers might come and whisk her away.* She loved this people and this place the more deeply perhaps because she was not of them. Forget the harsh things she has just said to Thol. He surely was to blame. And belike she would even have begged his pardon had she not been preoccupied with thoughts for the whole homeland, with great fears of what the dreadful dragon might be going to do when he woke up.

IV

And a wonder it was that he did not wake forthwith, so loud a bellow of terror did Brud and his dog utter at the glimpse they had of him. The glimpse sufficed them: both bounded to the foot of the hill with incredible speed, still howling. From the mouths of caves and huts people darted and stood agape. Responsive sheep, goats, geese, what not, made great noises of their own. Brud stood waving his arms wildly towards the hill. People stared from him to the column of smoke, and from it to him. They were still heavy with sleep. Unusual behaviour at any time annoyed them; they deeply resented behaviour so unusual as this so early in the morning. Little by little, disapproval merged into anxiety. Brud became the centre

* Lest the reader assume that in the course of this narrative one or both of Thia's parents will return to claim her, let me at once state that within a few months of her being left in the homeland her father was killed by a lion, and her mother by a lioness, in what has since become Shropshire.

of a circle. But he did not radiate conviction. A dragon ?
A dragon in the homeland ? Brud must be mad !

Brud called Thol to witness. Thol, afraid that if he told
the truth he would be beaten by everybody but Brud, said
nothing. Favourite Thia was not so reticent. She described
clearly the dragon's head and tail and the black path
through the grass. Something like panic passed around
the circle ; not actual panic, for—surely Thia's bright dark
eyes had deceived her. A dragon was one thing, the homeland another : there couldn't possibly be a dragon in the
homeland. Mainly that they might set Thia's mind at rest,
a few people went to reconnoitre. Presently, with palsied
lips, they were admitting that there could be, and was, a
dragon in the homeland.

They ran stuttering the news in all directions, ran knowing it to be true, yet themselves hardly believing it, ran
hoping others would investigate it and prove it a baseless
rumour, ran gibbering it to the very confines of the homeland. Slowly, incredulously, people from all quarters made
their way to the place where so many were already gathered.
The whole population was at length concentrated in what
is Berkeley Square. Up the sky the sun climbed steadily.
Surely, thought the homelanders, a good sign ? This god
of theirs could not look so calm and bright if there were
really a dragon among his chosen people ? Bold adventurers
went scouting hopefully up the hill, only to return with
horror in their eyes, and with the same old awful report
upon their lips. Before noon the whole throng was convinced. Eld is notoriously irreceptive of new ideas ; but
even the oldest inhabitant stood convinced now.

Silence reigned, broken only by the bleatings, cacklings,
quackings, of animals unreleased from their pens or coops,

far and near. Up, straight up through the windless air went the column of smoke steadfastly, horribly, up higher than the eyes of the homelanders could follow it.

What was to be done? Could nothing be done? Could not some one, at any rate, say something? People who did not know each other, or had for years not been on speaking terms, found themselves eagerly conversing, in face of the common peril. Solemn parties were formed to go and view the dragon's track, its odious scorched track from the marshes. People remembered having been told by wanderers that when a dragon swam a river he held high his head, lest his flames should be quenched. The river that had been crossed last night by this monster was a great god. Why had he not drowned the monster? Well, fire was a great god also, and he deigned to dwell in dragons. One god would not destroy another. But again, would even a small god deign to dwell in a dragon? The homelanders revised their theology. Fire was not a god at all.

Then, why, asked some, had the river not done his duty? The more rigid logicians answered that neither was the river a god. But this doctrine was not well received. People felt they had gone quite far enough as it was. Besides, now was a time rather for action than for thought. Some of those who were skilled in hunting went to fetch their arrows and spears, formed a sort of army, and marched round and round the lower slopes of the hill in readiness to withstand and slay the dragon so soon as he should come down into the open. At first this had a cheering and heartening effect (on all but Thol, whose personal aspiration you remember). But soon there recurred to the minds of many, and were repeated broadcast, other words that had been spoken by wanderers. 'So hard,' had said one, 'are the scales of a crawling dragon that no spear can prick him, howsoever sharp and heavy and strongly hurled.' And another had grimly said, 'Young is that dragon who is not older than the oldest man.' And another, 'A crawling dragon is not baulked but by the swiftness of men's heels.'

All this was most depressing. Confidence in the spearmen was badly shaken. The applause for them whenever they passed by was quieter, betokening rather pity than hope. Nay, there were people who now deprecated any attempt to kill the dragon. The dragon, they argued, must not be angered. If he were not mistreated he might do no harm. He had a right to exist. He had visited Gra's cave in a friendly spirit, but Gra had tried to mistreat him, and the result should be a lesson to them all.

Others said, more acceptably, 'Let us think not of the dragon. What the spearmen can do, that will they do. Let this day be as other days, and each man to the task that is his.' Brud was one of those who hurried away gladly. Nor was Thol loth to follow. The chance that the dragon might come out in his absence did not worry a boy so unprepared to-day for single combat; and if other hands than his were to succeed in slaying the dragon, he would liefer not have the bitterness of looking on.

Thia also detached herself from the throng. Many voices of men and women and children called after her, bidding her stay. 'I would find me some task,' she answered.

'O Thia,' said one, 'find only flowers for your hair. And sing to us, dance for us. Let this day be as other days.' And so pleaded many voices.

But Thia answered them, ' My heart is too sad. We are all in peril. For myself I am not afraid. But how should I dance, who love you ? Not again, O dear ones, shall I dance, until the dragon be slain or gone back across the water. Neither shall I put flowers in my hair nor sing.'

She went her way, and was presently guiding a flock of geese to a pond that does not exist now.

v

She sat watching the geese gravely, fondly, as they swam and dived and cackled. She was filled with a sense of duty to them. They too were homelanders and dear ones. She wished that all the others could be so unknowing and so happy.

A breeze sprang up, swaying the column of smoke and driving it across the valley, on which it cast a long, wide, dark shadow.

Thia felt very old. She remembered a happy and careless child who woke—how long ago !—and went looking for mushrooms. And this memory gave her another feeling. You see, she had eaten nothing all day.

Near the pond was a cherry-tree. She looked at it. She tried not to. This was no day for eating. The sight of the red cherries jarred on her. They were so very red. She went to the tree unwillingly. She hoped no one would see her. In your impatience at the general slowness of man's evolution, you will be glad to learn that Thia, climbing that tree and swinging among the branches, had notably more of assurance and nimble ease than any modern child would have in like case. It was only her mind that misgave her.

Ashamed of herself, ashamed of feeling so much younger and stronger now, she dropped to the ground and wondered how she was to atone. She chose the obvious course. She ran around the homeland urging every one to eat something. All were grateful for the suggestion. The length of their fast is the measure of the shock they had received that day, and of the strain imposed on them. Eating had ever been a thing they excelled in. Most of them were far too fat. Thia's suggestion was acted on with all speed. Great quantities of cold meat were consumed. And this was well. The night in store was to make special demands on the nerves of the homelanders.

As the sun drew near down to the west, the breeze dropped with it, and the smoke was again an upright column, reddened now by the sun. Later, while afterglow faded into twilight, to some of the homelanders it seemed that the base of the column was less steady, was moving. They were right. The time of their testing was at hand. The dragon was coming down the hill.

VI

The spearmen opened out their ranks quickly and hovered in skirmishing order. The dragon's pace was no quicker than that of a man strolling. His gait was at once ponderous and sinuous. The great body rocked on the four thick leglets that moved in a somehow light and stealthy fashion. They ended, these leglets, in webbed feet with talons. The long neck was craned straight forward, flush with the ground, but the tail, which was longer still, swung its barbed tip slowly from side to side, and sometimes rose, threshing the air. Neck, body and tail were surmounted by a ridge of upstanding spurs. In fact, the dragon was just what I have called him : dreadful.

Spears flew in the twilight. Ringing noises testified that many of them hit the mark. They rang as they glanced off the scales that completely sheathed the brute, who, now and again, coiled his neck round to have a look at them, as though they rather interested and amused him. One of them struck him full on the brow (if brow it can be called) without giving him an instant's pause.

Anon, however, he halted, rearing his neck straight up, turning his head slowly this way and that, and seemed to take, between his great puffs of fiery smoke, a general survey of the valley. Twilight was not fading into darkness, for a young moon rode the sky, preserving a good view for, and of, the dragon. Most of the homelanders had with one accord retired to the further side of the valley, across the dividing stream. Only the spearmen remained on the dragon's side, and some sheep that were in a fold there. One of the spearmen, taking aim, ventured rather near to the dragon—so near that the dragon's neck, shooting down, all but covered the distance. The clash of the dragon's jaws resounded. The spearman had escaped only by a hair's breadth. The homelanders made a faint noise, something between a sigh and a groan.

The dragon looked at them for a long time. He seemed to be in no hurry. He glanced at the moon, as though saying, ' The night is young.' He glanced at the sheep-fold and slowly went to it. Wanderers had often said of dragons that they devoured no kind of beast in any land that had human creatures in it. What would this dragon do? The huddled sheep bleated piteously at him. He reared his neck high and examined them from that altitude. Suddenly a swoop and a clash. The neck was instantly erect again, with a ripple down it. The head turned slowly towards the homelanders, then slowly away again. The mind was seemingly divided. There was a pause. This ended in another swoop, clash, recoil and ripple. Another dubious pause; and now, neck to ground, the dragon headed amain for the homelanders.

They drew back, they scattered. Some rushed they knew not whither for refuge, wailing wildly; others swarmed up the trunks of high trees (swiftlier, yes, than we could). Across the stream stepped the dragon with a sort of cumbrous daintiness, and straightway, at his full speed, which was that of a man walking quickly, gave chase. If you care for the topographical side of history, you should walk out of Berkeley Square by way of Charles Street, into Curzon Street, past Chesterfield House, up Park Lane, along Oxford Street, down South Molton Street and back into Berkeley Square by way of Bruton Street. This, roughly, was the dragon's line of route. He did not go exactly straight along it. He often swerved and zigzagged; and he made in the course of the night many long pauses. He would thrust his head into the mouth of some cave or hut, on the chance that some one had been so foolish as to hide there; or he would crane his neck up among the lower branches of a tall tree, scorching these with his breath, and peering up into the higher branches, where refugees might or might not be; or he would just stay prone somewhere, doing nothing. For the rest, he pursued whom he saw. High speed he never achieved ; but he had cunning, and had power to bewilder with fear. Before the night was out he was back again in his cave upon the hill. And the sleepless home-landers, forgathering in the dawn to hear and tell what things had befallen, gradually knew themselves to be the fewer by five souls.

VII

It is often said that no ills are so hard to suffer as to anticipate. I do not know that this is true. But it does seem to be a fact that people comport themselves better under the incidence of an ill than under the menace of it ; better also in their fear of an ill's recurrence than when the ill is first feared. Some of the homelanders, you will have felt, had been rather ridiculous on the first day of the dragon's presence among them. They had not been so in the watches of the night. Even Brud and his dog had shown signs of courage and endurance. Even Thol had not cried much. Thia had behaved perfectly. But this is no more than you would expect of Thia. The point is that after their panic at the dragon's first quick onset, the generality of the homelanders had behaved well. And now, haggard though they were in the dawn, wan, dishevelled, they were not without a certain collective dignity.

When everything had been told and heard, they stood for a while in silent mourning. The sun rose from the hills over the water, and with a common impulse they knelt to this great god, beseeching him that he would straightway call the dragon back beyond those hills, never to return.

Then they looked up at the cave. To-day the dragon was wholly inside, his smoke rolling up from within the cave's mouth. Long looked the homelanders for that glimmer of nether fire which would show that he was indeed moving forth. There was nothing for them to see but the black smoke. ' Peradventure,' said one, ' the sun is not a god.' ' Nay,' said another, ' rather may it be that he is so great a god that we cannot know his purposes, nor he be turned aside from them by our small woes.' This was accounted a strange but a wise saying. ' Nevertheless,' said the sayer, ' it is well that we should ask help of him in woes that to us are not small.' So again the homelanders prayed, and though their prayer was still unanswered they felt themselves somehow strengthened.

It was agreed that they should disperse to their dwellings, eat, and presently reassemble in formal council.

And here I should mention Shib ; for he was destined to be important in this council, though he was but a youth, and on his cheeks and chin the down had but begun to lengthen. I may as well also mention Veo, his brother, elder than him by one year. They were the sons of Oc and Loga, with whom they lived in a cave near the valley. Veo had large eyes which seemed to see nothing, but saw much. Shib had small eyes which seemed to see much, and saw it. Shib's parents thought him very clever, as indeed he was. They thought Veo a fool ; but Mr. Roger Fry, had he seen the mural drawings in their cave, would have assured them that he was a master.

Said Veo to Shib, as they followed their parents to the cave, ' Though I prayed that he might not, I am glad that the dragon abides with us. His smoke is as the trunk of a great tree whose branches are the sky. When he comes crawling down the hill he is more beautiful than Thia dancing.'

Shib's ideas about beauty were academic. Thia dancing, with a rose-bush on one side of her and a sunset on the other, was beautiful. The dragon was ugly. But Shib was not going to waste breath in argument with his absurd brother. What mattered was not that the dragon was ugly, but that the dragon was a public nuisance, to be abated if it could not be suppressed. The spearmen had failed to suppress it, and would continue to fail. But Shib thought he saw a way to abatement. He had carefully watched throughout the night the dragon's demeanour. He had noted how, despite so many wanderers' clear testimony as to the taste of all dragons, this creature had seemed to palter in choice between the penned sheep near to him and the mobile people across the stream ; noted that despite the great talons on his feet he did not attempt to climb any of the trees ; noted the long rests he took here and there. On these observations Shib had formed a theory, and on this theory a scheme. And during the family meal in the cave he recited the speech he was going to make at the council. His parents were filled with admiration. Veo, however, did not listen to a word. Nor did he even attend the council. He stayed in the cave, making with a charred stick, on all vacant spaces, stark but spirited pictures of the dragon.

VIII

I will not report in even an abridged form the early proceedings of the council. For they were tedious. The speakers were many, halting, and not to the point. Shib, when his chance at length came, shone. He had a dry, unattractive manner; but he had something to say, he said it clearly and tersely, and so he held his audience.

Having stated the facts he had noted, he claimed no certainty for the deduction he had made from them. He did not say, 'Know then surely, O homelanders, that this is a slothful dragon.' Nor, for the matter of that, did he say he had furnished a working hypothesis, or a hypothesis that squared with the known facts, or a hypothesis that held the field. Such phrases, alas, were impossible in the simple and barbarous tongue of the homelanders. But 'May it not be,' Shib did say, 'that this is a slothful dragon?' There was a murmur of meditative assent. 'Hearken then,' said Shib, 'to my counsel. Let the spearmen go slay two deer. Let the shepherds go slay two sheep, and the goat-herds two goats. Also let there be slain three geese and as many ducks. Or ever the sun leave us, and the dragon wake from his sleep, let us take all these up and lay them at the mouth of the cave that was Gra's cave. Thus it may be that this night shall not be as the last was, but we all asleep and safe. And if so it betide us, let us make to the dragon other such offerings to-morrow, and on all days that are to come.'

There was prompt and unanimous agreement that this plan should be tried. The spearmen went hunting. Presently they returned with a buck and a roe. By this time the other animals prescribed had been slain in due number. It remained that the feast should be borne noiselessly up the hill and spread before the slumbering dragon. The homelanders surprised one another, surprised even themselves, by their zeal for a share of this task. Why should any one of them be wanting to do work that others could do? and willing to take a risk that others would take? Really they did not know. It was a strange foible. But there it was. A child can carry the largest of ducks; but as many as four men were lending a hand in porterage of a duck to-day. Not one of the porters enjoyed this work. But somehow they all wanted to do it, and did it with energy and good humour.

Very soon, up yonder on the flat shelf of ground in front of the cave's mouth, lay temptingly ranged in a semicircular pattern two goats, three ducks, two deer, three geese and two sheep. All had been done that was to be done. The homelanders suddenly began to feel the effects of their sleepless night. They would have denied that they were sleepy, but they felt a desire to lie down and think. The valley soon had a coverlet of sleeping figures, prone and supine. But, as you know, the mind has a way of waking us when it should; and the home-landers were all wide awake when the shadows began to lengthen.

Very still the air was; and very still stood those men and women and children, on the other side of the dividing stream. The sun, setting red behind them, sent their shadows across the stream, on and on slowly, to the very foot of the hill up to which they were so intently looking. The column of smoke, little by little, lost its flush. But anon it showed fitful glimpses of a brighter red at the base of it, making known that the dragon's head was not inside the cave. And now it seemed to the homelanders, in these long moments, that their hearts ceased beating, and all hope died in them. Suddenly—clash! the dragon's jaws echoed all over the valley; and then what silence!

Through the veil of smoke, dimly, it was seen that the red glow rose, paused, fell—clash ! again.

Twelve was a number that the homelanders could count up to quite correctly. Yet even after the twelfth clash they stood silent and still. Not till the red glow faded away into the cave did they feel sure that to-night all was well with them.

Then indeed a great deep sigh went up from the throng. There were people who laughed for joy ; others who wept for the same reason. None was happier than Thia. She was on the very point of singing and dancing, but remembered her promise, and the exact wording of it, just in time. In all the valley there was but one person whose heart did not rejoice. This was Veo. He had come out late in the afternoon, to await, impatiently, the dragon's reappearance. He had particularly wanted to study the action of the hind-legs, which he felt he had not caught rightly. Besides, he had wanted to see the whole magnificent creature again, just for the sight of it. Veo was very angry. Nobody, however, heeded him. Everybody heeded the more practical brother. It was a great evening for Oc and Loga. They were sorry there was a dragon in the homeland, but even more (for parents will be parents) were they proud of their boy's success. The feelings of Thol, too, were not unmixed. Though none of the homelanders, except Thia, had ever shown him any kindness, he regretted the dragon, and was very glad that the dragon was not coming out to-night ; but he was even gladder that the dragon had not been slain by the spearmen nor called back across the water by the sun. It was true that if either of these things had happened he could have gone to sleep comfortably in his own cave, and that he dared not sleep there now, and saw no prospect of sleeping there at all until he had slain the dragon. But he bethought him of the many empty caves on the way down to the marshes. And he moved into that less fashionable quarter—sulkily indeed, but without tears, and sustained by a great faith in the future.

IX

On the morning of next day the homelanders prayed again to the sun that he would call the dragon away from them. He did not so. Therefore they besought him that he would forbid the dragon to come further than the cave's mouth, and would cause him to be well-pleased with a feast like yesterday's.

Such a feast, in the afternoon, was duly laid at the cave's mouth ; and again, when the sun was setting, the dragon did not come down the hill, but ate aloft there, and at the twelfth clash drew back his glowing jaws into the cave.

Day followed day, each with the same ritual and result.

Shib did not join in the prayers. He regarded them as inefficacious, and also as rather a slight to himself. The homelanders, be it said, intended no slight. They thought Shib wonderfully clever, and were most grateful to him ; but it never occurred to them to rank him among gods.

Veo always prayed heartily that the dragon should be called away forthwith. He wanted to see the dragon by daylight. But he did not pray that the dragon should not come forth in the evening. Better a twilit dragon than none at all.

Little Thol, though he prayed earnestly enough that the

dragon should stay at home by night, never prayed for him to leave the homeland. He prayed that he himself might grow up very quickly, and be very big and very strong and very clever and very brave.

For the rest, the homelanders were all orthodox in their devotions.

X

The young moon had grown old, had dwindled, and disappeared. The sound of the clashed jaws ceased to be a novelty. The vesperal gatherings in the valley became smaller. The great column of smoke, by day and by night, was for the homelanders a grim reminder of what had happened, and of what would happen again if once they failed to fulfil the needs of their uninvited guest. They were resolved that they would not fail. In this resolution they had a sombre sense of security. But there came, before the leaves of the trees were yellow, an evening when the dragon left untasted the feast spread for him, and crawled down the hill. He was half-way down before any one noticed his coming. And on that night, a longer night than the other, he made a wider journey around the homeland, and took a heavier toll of lives.

Thenceforth always, at sunset, guards were posted to watch the hill and to give, if need were, the alarm. Nor did even this measure suffice. In the dawn of a day in winter, when snow was lying thick on the homeland, a goat-herd observed with wonder a wide pathway through the snow from the dragon's cave ; and presently he saw afar on the level ground the dragon himself, with his head inside the mouth of a lonely hut that was the home of a young man recently wedded. From the hut's mouth crept forth clouds of smoke, and, as the dragon withdrew his head, the goat-herd, finding voice, raised such a cry as instantly woke many sleepers. That day lived long in the memory of the homelanders. The dragon was very active. He did not plod through the snow. He walked at his full speed upon the ground, the snow melting before him at the approach of his fiery breath. It was the homelanders that plodded. Some of them stumbled head foremost into snowdrifts and did not escape their pursuer. There was nothing slothful in the dragon's conduct that day. Hour after hour in the keen frosty air he went his way, and not before nightfall did he go home.

Thus was inaugurated what we may call the Time of Greater Stress. No one could know at what hour of night or day the dragon might again raid the homeland. Relays of guards had to watch the hill always. No one, lying down to sleep, knew that the dragon might not forthcome before sunrise ; no one, throughout the day, knew that the brute might not be forthcoming at any moment. True, he forthcame seldom. The daily offerings of slain beasts and birds sufficed him, mostly. But he was never to be depended on—never.

Shib's name somewhat fell in the general esteem. Nor was it raised again by the execution of a scheme that he conceived. The roe and buck stuffed with poisonous herbs were swallowed by the dragon duly, but the column of smoke from the cave's mouth did not cease that evening, as had been hoped. And on the following afternoon— a sign that the stratagem had not been unnoticed—one of the men who were placing the food in front of the cave perished miserably in the dragon's jaws.

Other devices of Shib's failed likewise. The home-landers had to accept the dragon as a permanent factor in their lives. Year by year, night and day, rose the sinister column of smoke, dense, incessant. Happy those tiny children who knew not what a homeland without a dragon was like! So, at least, thought the elders.

And yet, were these elders so much less happy than they had erst been? Were they not—could they but have known it—happier? Did not the danger in which they lived make them more appreciative of life? Surely they had a zest that in the halcyon days was not theirs? Certainly they were quicker-witted. They spoke less slowly, their eyes were brighter, all their limbs nimbler. Perhaps this was partly because they ate less meat. The dragon's diet made it necessary that they should somewhat restrict their own, all the year round. The dragon, without knowing it, was a good physician to them.

Without being a moralist or a preacher, he had also improved their characters. Quarrels had become rare. Ill-natured gossip was frowned on. Suspicions throve not. Manners had unstiffened. The homelanders now liked one another. They had been drawn charmingly together in brotherhood and sisterhood. You would have been surprised at the change in them.

XI

But for his bright red hair, perhaps you would not have recognised Thol at all. He was a great gawky youth now. Spiritually, however, he had changed little. He was still intent on slaying the dragon.

In the preceding years he had thought of little else than this, and as he never had said a word about it he was not accounted good company. Nor had he any desire to shine —in any light but that of a hero. The homelanders would have been cordial enough to him, throughout those years, if he had wished them to be so. But he never was able to forget how cold and unkind they had been to him in his early childhood. It was not for their sake that he had so constantly nursed and brooded over his great wish. It was for his own sake only.

An unsympathetic character? Stay!—let me tell you that since the dawn of his adolescence another sake had come in to join his own : Thia's sake.

From the moment when she, in childhood, had called him a coward, it always had been Thia especially that he wished to impress. But in recent times his feeling had changed. How should such a lout as he ever hope to impress Thia, who was a goddess? Thol hoped only to make Thia happy, to see her go dancing and singing once more, with flowers in her hair. Thol did not even dare hope that Thia would thank him. Thol was not an unsympathetic character at all.

As for Thia, she was more fascinating than ever. Do not be misled by her seeming to Thol a goddess. Remember that the homelanders worshipped cherry trees and rain and fire and running water and all such things. There was nothing of the statuesque Hellenic ideal about Thia. She had not grown tall, she was as lissom and almost as slight as ever ; and her alien dark hair had not lost its wildness : on windy days it flew out far behind her, like a thunder cloud, and on calm days hid her as in a bush. She had never changed the task that she chose on the day of the dragon's advent. She was still a goose-girl. But perhaps she was conscious now that the waddling gait of her geese made the grace of her own gait the lovelier by its contrast. Certainly she was familiar with her face. She had often leaned over clear pools to study it—to see what the home-landers saw in it. She was very glad of her own charms because they were so dear to all those beloved people. But sometimes her charms also saddened her. She had had many suitors—youths of her own age, and elder men too. Even Veo, thinking her almost as beautiful as the dragon, had laid his hands upon her shoulders, in the ritual mode. Even the intellectual Shib had done so. And even from such elders as these it was dreadful to turn away. Nor was Thia a girl of merely benevolent nature : she had warm desires, and among the younger suitors more than one had much pleased her fancy. But stronger than any other sentiment in her was her love for the homeland. Not until the dragon were slain or were gone away across the waters would Thia be wife of any man.

So far as she knew, she had sentenced herself to per-petual maidenhood. Even had she been aware of Thol's inflexible determination, she would hardly have become hopeful. Determination is one thing, doing is another.

The truth of that old adage sometimes forced itself on poor Thol himself, as he sat watching the sheep that he herded near his cave on the way to the marshes ; and at such time his sadness was so great that it affected even his sheep, causing them to look askance at him and bleat piteously, and making drearier a neighbourhood that was in itself dreary.

But, one day in the eighteenth summer of his years, Thol ceased to despond. There came, wet from the river and mossy from the marshes, an aged wanderer. He turned his dark eyes on Thol and said with a smile, pointing towards the thick smoke on the hill, ' A dragon is here now ? '

' Yea, O wanderer,' Thol answered.

' There was none aforetime,' said the old man. ' A dragon was what your folk needed.'

' They need him not. But tell me, O you that have so much wandered, and have seen many dragons, tell me how a dragon may be slain ! '

' Mind your sheep, young shepherd. Let the dragon be. Let not your sheep mourn you.'

' They shall not. I shall slay the dragon. Only tell me how ! Surely there is a way ? '

' It is a way that would lead you into his jaws, O fool, and not hurt him. Only through the roof of his mouth can a dragon be pierced and wounded. He opens not his jaws save when they are falling upon his prey. Do they not fall swiftly, O fool ? '

' O wanderer, yea. But '——

' Could you deftly spear the roof of that great mouth, O prey, in that little time ? '

' Yea, surely, if so the dragon would perish.'

The old man laughed. ' So would the dragon perish, truly ; but so only. So would be heard what few ears have heard—the cry that a dragon utters as he is slain. But so only.' And the old man went his way northward.

From that day on, Thol did not watch his sheep very much. They, on the other hand, spent most of their time in watching him. They rather thought he was mad, standing in that odd attitude and ever lunging his crook up at one of the nodding boughs of that ash-tree.

Twice in the course of the autumn the dragon came down the hill; but when the watchmen sounded the alarm Thol did not go forth to meet him. He was not what his flock thought him.

He had now exchanged his crook for a spear—a straight well-seasoned sapling of oak, with a long sharp head of flint. With this, day by day, hour after hour, he lunged up at the boughs of fruit-trees. His flock, deploring what seemed to them mania, could not but admire his progressive skill. Rarely did he fail now in piercing whatever plum or apple he aimed at.

When winter made bare the branches, it was at the branches that Thol aimed his thrusts. His accuracy was unerring now. But he had yet to acquire the trick of combining the act of transfixion with the act of leaping aside. Else would he perish even in victory.

Spring came. As usual, her first care was to put blossoms along the branches of such almond trees as were nearest to the marshes.

The ever side-leaping Thol pricked off any little single blossom that he chose.

XII

Spring was still active in the homeland when, one day, a little while before sunset, the watchers of the hill blew their horns. There came from all quarters the usual concourse of young and old, to watch the direction of the dragon and to keep out of it. Down came the familiar great beast, the never-ageing dragon, picking his way into the green valley. And he saw an unwonted sight there. He saw somebody standing quite still on the nearer bank of the stream; a red-haired young person, holding a spear. About this young person he formed a theory which had long been held by certain sheep.

Little wonder that the homelanders also formed that theory! Little wonder that they needed no further proof of it when, deaf to the cries of entreaty that they uttered through the evening air, Thol stood his ground!

Slowly, as though to give the wretched young lunatic a chance, the dragon advanced.

But quickly, very terribly and quickly, when he was within striking distance, he reared his neck up. An instant later there rang through the valley—there seemed to rend the valley—a single screech, unlike anything that its hearers had ever heard.

Those who dared to look saw the vast length of the dragon, neck on grass, coiling slowly round. The tip of the tail met the head and parted from it. Presently the vast length was straight, motionless.

Yet even of those who had dared look none dared believe that the dragon was indeed dead.

But for its death-cry, Thol himself would hardly have believed.

The second firm believer was Thia. Thia, with swift conviction, plucked some flowers and put them loosely into her hair. Thia, singing as well as though she had never ceased to sing, and dancing as prettily as though she had for years been practising her steps, went singing and dancing towards the stream. Lightly she leapt the stream, and then very seriously and quietly walked to the spot where Thol stood. She looked up at him, and then, without a word, raised her arms and put her hands upon his shoulders. He, who had slain the dragon, trembled.

' O Thol,' she said gently, ' you turn not away from me, but neither do you raise me from the ground.'

Then Thol raised Thia thrice from the ground.

And he said, ' Let our home be the cave that was my father's.'

Hand in hand, man and wife, they went up the hill, and round to the eastern side of its summit. But when they came to the mouth of the old cave there, he paused and let go her hand.

' O Thia,' he said wonderingly, ' is it indeed true that you love me ? '

' O Thol,' she answered, ' it is most true.'

' O Thia,' he said, ' love me always ! '

' I have long ceased to love you, O Thol,' she said, five years later, in a low voice. But I see that I have out-stripped my narrative. I must hark back.

XIII

The sun had already risen far when Thol and Thia were wakened by a continuous great hum as of many voices. When they looked forth and down from the mouth of their high home, it seemed to them that all the homelanders were there beneath them, gazing up.

And this was indeed so. Earlier in the morning, by force of habit, all the homelanders had gone to what we call Berkeley Square, the place where for so many years they had daily besought the sun to call the dragon away across the waters. There, where lay the great smokeless and harmless carcass, was no need for prayers now ; and with one accord the throng had moved from the western to the eastern foot of the hill, and stayed there gazing in reverence up to the home of a god greater than the sun.

When at length the god showed himself, there arose from the throng a great roar of adoration. The throng went down on its knees to him, flung up its arms to him, half-closed its eyes so as not to be blinded by the sight of him. His little mortal mate, knowing not that he was a god, thinking only that he was a brave man and her own, was astonished at the doings of her dear ones. The god himself, sharing her ignorance, was deeply embarrassed, and he blushed to the roots of his hair.

' Laugh, O Thol,' she whispered to him. ' It were well for them that you should laugh.' But he never had laughed in all his life, and was much too uncomfortable to begin doing so just now. He backed into the cave. The religious throng heaved a deep moan of disappointment as he did so. Thia urged him to come forth and laugh as she herself was doing. ' Nay,' he said, ' but do you, whom they love, dance a little for them and sing. Then will they go away happy.'

It seemed to Thia that really this was the next best plan, and so, still laughing, she turned round and danced and sang with great animation and good-will. The audience, however, was cold. It gave her its attention, but even this, she began to feel, was not its kind attention. Indeed, the audience was jarred. After a while—for Thia's pride forbade her to stop her performance—the audience began to drift away.

There were tears in her eyes when she danced back into the cave. But these she brushed away, these she forgot instantly in her lover's presence.

XIV

Love is not all. ' I must go drive my geese,' said the bride.

' And I my sheep,' said the bridegroom.

' There is good grass, O Thol, round my geese's pond. Let your sheep graze there always. Thus shall not our work sever us.'

As they went forth, some children were coming up the hill, carrying burdens. The burdens were cold roast flesh, dried figs, and a gourd of water, sent by some elders as a votive offering to the god. The children knelt at sight of the god and then ran shyly away, leaving their gifts on the ground. The god and his mate feasted gladly. Then they embraced and parted, making tryst at the pond.

When Thia approached the pond, she did not wonder that Thol was already there, for sheep go quicker than geese. But—where were his sheep? ' Have they all strayed?' she cried out to him.

He came to meet her, looking rather foolish.

' O Thia,' he explained, ' as I went to the fold, many men and women were around it. I asked them what they did there. They knelt and made answer, " We were gazing at the sheep that had been the god's." When I made to unpen the flock, there was a great moaning. There was gnashing of teeth, O Thia, and tearing of hair. It was said by all that the god must herd sheep nevermore.'

' And you, beloved, what said you?'

' I said nothing, O Thia, amid all that wailing. I knew not what to say.'

Thia laughed long but tenderly. 'And your sheep, beloved, what said they?'

'How should I know?' asked Thol.

'And you left them there? Do you not love them?'

'I have never loved them.'

'But they were your task?'

'O Thia, the dragon was my task.'

She stroked his arm. 'The dragon is dead, O Thol. You have slain the dragon, O my brave dear one. That task is done. You must find some other. All men must work. Since you loved not your sheep, you shall love my geese, and I will teach you to drive them with me.'

'That,' said Thol, 'would not be a man's work, O Thia.'

'But they say you are a god! And I think a god may do as he will.'

Her flock had swum out into the pond. She called it back to her, and headed it away towards some willows. From one of these she plucked for Thol a long twig such as she herself carried, and, having stripped it of its leaves, gave it to him and began to teach him her art.

XV

There was, as Thia had known there must be, a great concourse of people around and about the dragon.

There was a long line of children riding on its back; there were infants in arms being urged by their mothers never to forget that they had seen it; there were many young men and women trying to rip off some of its scales, as reminders; and there were elders exchanging reminiscences of its earliest raids and correcting one another on various points. And the whole crowd of holiday-makers was so intent that the gradual approach of that earnest worker, Thol, was not noticed until he came quite near.

Very gradual, very tortuous and irregular, his approach was. Thia, just now, was letting him shift for himself, offering no hints at all. For the homelanders' sake, she wished him to be seen at his worst. It was ill that they should worship a false god. To her, he was something better than a real god. But this was another matter. To the homelanders, he ought to seem no more than a man who had done a great deed and set a high example. And for his own sake, and so for hers—for how could his not be hers?—she wished him to have no more honour than vas his due. Splendid man though he was, and only a year younger than herself, he was yet a child ; and children, thought Thia—though she was conscious that she herself, for all the petting she had received, was rather perfect— are easily spoilt. Altogether, the goose-girl's motives were as pure as her perception was keen. Admirable, too, were her tactics ; and they should have succeeded. Yet they failed. In the eyes of the homelanders the goose-god lost not a jot of his divinity.

No hint of disillusion was in the moans evoked by the sight of him. Grief, shame, horror at his condescension, and a deep wrath against the whilom darling Thia, were all that was felt by the kneeling and swaying crowd.

Thia knew it. She was greatly disappointed. Indeed, she was near to shedding tears again. Pride saved her from that. Besides, she was angry, and not only angry but amused. And in a clear voice that was audible above the collective moaning, ' Have patience, O homelanders,' she cried. ' He is new to his work. He will grow in skill. These geese will find that he is no fool. And it may be that hereafter, if you are all very good, I will teach him to sing and dance for you, with flowers in his bright red hair.'

Having thus spoken, she ran to overtake her husband, and soon, guiding the flock in good order, went her way with him back to the pond.

XVI

There was a general desire that the dragon should not be buried anywhere within the confines of the homeland. Shib conceived that if the trunks of felled trees were used as rollers the carcass might be transported to the swamps and be sunk there. By its vast weight the carcass frustrated this scheme. A long deep trench must be dug beside it. All the able-bodied men of the homeland offered their services, and of course Shib was a most efficient director of the work.

You will be glad to hear that Shib was a more sympathetic character than he once was. The public spirit that had always been his was unmarred now by vanity and personal ambition. He was a quiet, disinterested, indefatigable worker for the common weal, burning always with that hard, gem-like flame which Mr. Pater discerned in the breasts of our own Civil Servants. He had forgotten, or he remembered without bitterness, the time when he was a popular hero. Thol's great deed was a source of genuine pleasure to him. Nay (for he had long ago outgrown his callow atheism), he accepted Thol as a god, though he was too cautious to rate him higher than the sun.

Thus he was much shocked when Thol came wishing to help in the labour. Rising, at Thol's earnest entreaty, from his knees, he ventured to speak firmly to the god—reverently but very firmly pointing out to him that the labourers, if their religious feelings were flouted, would probably cease work; and he hinted that he himself would have to consider whether he could retain his post. So Thol went back to the goose-pond and was so much chidden by Thia for his weakness that he almost wished she believed him to be a god. Of course he was not a god. Of course Thia was right. Still, Shib was known to be a very wise man. It was strange that Shib should be mistaken. Inwardly, he could not agree with Thia that Shib was a fool. And I think she must have suspected him of this reservation, for she looked at him with much trouble in her eyes and was for a while silent, and then, fondlingly, made him promise that he never would trust any one's thoughts but hers.

Three days later the great trench was finished; and down into it, by leverage of many stakes heftily wielded in unison, was heaved the dragon (and there, to this day, deep down under the eastern side of the garden and roadway of Berkeley Square, is the dragon's skeleton—an occult memorial of Thol's deed). Down into the trench, with a great thud that for a moment shook the ground, fell Thol's victim. Presently the trench brimmed with earth, and this earth was stamped firm by exultant feet, and more earth was added to it and stamped on till only a long brown path, that would soon be green and unnoticeable, marked the place of sepulture.

The great occasion lacked only the god's presence. Of course the god had been invited. Shib, heading a deputation on the banks of the goose-pond, had besought him that he would deign to throw the first clod of earth upon the dragon ; and he had diplomatically added that all the homelanders were hoping that Thia might be induced to sing and dance on the grave as soon as it had been filled. But Thia had answered that she could not give her husband leave, inasmuch as he had been idle at his work that day ; he would like very much to come ; but it was for that very reason that she would not let him : he must be punished. As for herself, she too would very much like to come, but she must stay and keep him to his work. Thol saying nothing, the deputation had then withdrawn, not without many obeisances, which Thia, with as many curtseys, roguishly took to herself.

However, even without the light of the god's countenance on it, the festival was a great and glorious one. Perhaps indeed the revellers enjoyed themselves more than would have been possible in the glare of that awful luminary. The revels lasted throughout the night, and throughout the next day, and did not cease even then. Dazed with sleepiness and heavy with surfeits of meat, the homelanders continued to caper around bonfires and to clap one another on the back ; and only because they had not the secret of fermented liquor were there no regrettable scenes of intoxication. The revels had become a habit. It seemed as though they would never cease. But human strength is finite.

Thia would have liked to be in the midst of the great to-do. It was well that the homelanders should rejoice. And the homelanders were as dear to her as ever, though she had so much offended them for Thol's sake and theirs. Thol's nature was not social, as hers was ; but she knew that even he would have liked to have glimpses of the fun. It grieved her to keep him aloof with her among the geese. She sang and danced round him and petted him and made much of him, all day long.

XVII

The autumn was rainy ; and the winter was rainy too ; and thus the brown path over the dragon's grave vanished even before spring came. Green also was the grass that had for so many years been black above and around the mouth of the dragon's cave. Valley and hill smiled as blandly at each other as though they had never seen a dragon.

Little by little, likewise, the souls of the homelanders had reverted, as we should say, to type. There were no signs now of that mutual good-will which had been implanted in them by the common peril and had over-flowed so wildly at the time when the peril ended. Mistrust-fulness had revived, and surliness with it, and quickness to take offence, and a dull eagerness to retaliate on the offender. The shortcomings of others were once more the main preoccupation of the average homelander. Next to these, the weather was once more the favourite topic of conversation, especially if the weather were bad ; but even if it were good, the prospect of bad weather was dwelt on with a more than sufficient emphasis. Work, of course, had to be done ; but as little of it was done as might be, and that glumly, and not well. Meals were habitually larger than appetites. Eyes were duller, complexions less clear, chests narrower, stomachs more obtrusive, arms and legs less well-developed, than they had been under the dragon's auspices. And prayers, of course, were not said now.

Thia in her childhood had thought the homelanders perfect; and thus after the coming of the dragon she had observed no improvement in them. But now, with maturer vision, she did see that they were growing less worthy of high esteem. This grieved her. She believed that she loved the homelanders as much as ever, she told herself truly enough that it was much her own fault that they had ceased to love her. In point of fact, their coldness to her, in course of time, cooled her feeling for them: she was human. What she did love as much as ever was the homeland. What grieved her was that the homeland should have an imperfect population.

She talked constantly to Thol about her sorrow. He was not a very apt auditor. Being a native of the homeland, he could not see it, as she could, from without. It was not to him an idea, as it was to Thia's deep alien eyes. It was just the homeland. As for the homelanders themselves, he had never, as you may remember, loved them; but he liked them quite well now. He supposed he really was not a god; but it no longer embarrassed him to be thought so; indeed it pleased him to be thought so. The homelanders no longer knelt when he passed by. He had asked them not to, and they reverently obeyed his wish. He supposed Thia was right in saying that they were less good than in the days of the dragon; but in those days he had hardly known them. He was glad to know them better now. His nature had, in fact, become more expansive. He wished

Thia were not so troubled about the homeland. He wished she would think more gently of the homelanders, and think less about them, and talk less to him about them.

Sometimes she even tried to enlist his help. 'To me,' she would say, 'they would not hearken. But you, O Thol, whom in their folly they still believe to be a god, could give light to them and shame them back to goodness and strength, and so to happiness. I would teach you what words to say.' But Thol, even though he was to be spared the throes of composition, would look so blankly wretched that Thia's evangelical ardour was quenched in laughter. He did not know why she was laughing, and he hoped it was not at him that she was laughing : after all, he had slain the dragon. Nevertheless, her gaiety was a relief to him.

But her ardour was always flaming up again.

XVIII

She had very soon exempted him from that task which failed to cure the homelanders of their delusion about him. She agreed that goose-driving was not a man's work. As he did not wish to be a shepherd again, and as it was needful for his own good that he should be set to some sort of work, she urged him to be a goat-herd. Goats, she said, were less dull than sheep ; fiercer ; more like dragons. So, beside the goose-pond, he herded goats ; but without the enthusiasm that she had hoped for.

One day, about a year after their marriage, he even suggested that he should have a lad to help him. She said, with a curl of the lip, that she had not known he was old and feeble. He replied, seriously, that he was younger than she ; and, as for feebleness, he asked her to remember that he, not she, had slain the dragon. He then walked away, leaving his goats to their own devices, and his wife to hers, and spent the rest of the day in company that was more appreciative of him. He returned of course before sundown, fearful of a lecture. Thia, who had already driven his goats into their pen, did but smile demurely, saying that she would always be glad to do his work for him, and that she was trustier than any lad.

But, as time went on, her temper was not always so sweet. Indeed, it ceased to be sweet. In his steady, rather bovine way, he loved her as much as ever ; but his love of being with her was less great, and his pleasure in the society of others was greater, than of yore. Perhaps if Thia had borne a child, she might have been less troubled about the welfare of the homelanders. But this diversion and solace was not granted. Thia's maternal instinct had to spend itself on a community which she could not help and did not now genuinely love, and on a husband who did not understand her simplest thoughts and was moreover growing fat. Her disposition suffered under the strain. One day, when she was talking to him about the homeland, she paused with sudden suspicion and asked him what she had said last ; and he could make no answer ; and she asked him to tell her what he had been thinking about ; and he said that he had been thinking about his having slain the dragon ; and she, instead of chiding him tenderly, as she would have done in the old days, screamed. She screamed that she would go mad if ever again he spoke to her of that old dragon. She flung her arms out towards the hills across the waters and said, with no lowering of her voice, that every day, out yonder, men were slaying dragons and thinking nothing of it, and doing their work, and not growing fat. He asked her whether she meant that he himself was growing fat. 'Yea,' she answered. He said that then indeed she was mad. Away he strode, nor did he return at sundown; and it was late in the night before the god retired from a cheery party of worshippers and went up to the cave, where Thia, faintly visible in the moonlight, lay sleeping, with a look of deep disdain on her face.

XIX

Sometimes Thia wondered whether in her childhood the characters and ways of the homelanders had been as they were now. She hated to think that they had not been perfect in those days; but she reasoned that they could not have been: before the coming of the dragon they must have been as they were now, and the only difference was that they had then loved her. Thus even the memory of her bright careless early years was embittered to her.

In point of fact, the homelanders had not been exactly as they now were. The sudden cessation of the strain imposed on them by the dragon's presence, and of the comparative hardships also imposed by it, had caused a reaction so strong as to restore to them in a rather accentuated form what faults had originally been theirs. Human nature had grown rather more human than ever. Labour was a less than ever alluring thing. Responsibilities had a greater irksomeness. Freedom was all. And, as having special measure of vital force, especially were youths and maidens intent on making the most of their freedom. Their freedom was their religion ; and, as every religion needs rites, they ritualistically danced. They danced much during the day, and then much by moonlight or starlight or firelight, in a grim and purposeful, an angular and indeflexible manner, making it very clear that they were not to be trifled with.

Thia, when first she saw them engaged thus, had been very glad ; she imagined that they must be doing something useful. When she realised that they were dancing, she drew a deep breath. She remembered how she herself had danced—danced thoughtlessly and anyhow, from her heart, with every scrap of her body. She blushed at the recollection. She did not wonder that the homelanders had resented her dance on the morning after her marriage. She wondered that they had so encouraged her to dance when she was a child. And she felt that there must, after all, be in these young people a deep fund of earnestness, auguring well for their future.

Time had not confirmed this notion. The young people danced through the passing seasons and the passing years with ever greater assiduity and solemnity ; but other forms of seriousness were not manifested by them. Few of them seemed to find time even for falling in love and marrying. They all, however, called one another ' beloved,' and had a kind of mutual good-will which their elders, among themselves, would have done well to emulate. And for those elders they had a tolerant feeling which ought to have been, yet was not, fully reciprocated.

Thol within five years of the dragon's death, Thol with his immense red beard and his stately deportment, was of course very definitely an elder ; and still more so was that wife of his, that rather beautiful dark woman, Thia, whose face was so set and stern that she looked almost as though she—she !—were dancing. Thol was liked by the young people. They made much of him. They did not at all object to his being rather pompous : after all, he had slain that dragon, and they thought it quite natural that their parents should imagine he was a god. They liked him to be pompous. They humoured him. They enjoyed drawing him out. Among the youths there were several who, in the hours not devoted to earnest dancing and cursory guardianship of flocks, made pictures upon white stones or upon slabs of chalk. They liked especially to make pictures of Thol, because he was so ready to pose for them, and because he stood so still for them. They drew in a manner of their own, a manner which made the veins of poor old Veo stand out upon his forehead, and moved him to declare that they would die young and would die in shame and in agony. Thol, however, was no critic. He was glad to be portrayed in any manner. And it much pleased him to have the colour of his mane and beard praised constantly by the young artists. He had supposed the colour was wrong. Thia had been wont to laugh at it, in her laughing days. Thia had never called him beautiful, in her praising days. It gladdened him that there were now many young women—Afa, for instance, and Ola, and Ispa, and Moa—who called him, to his face, ' terribly ' beautiful.

Thol's face, which Thia had admired for its steadfast look, and later had begun to like less for its heavy look, had now a look that was rather fatuous. Afa and the others did not at all object to this. They liked it ; they encouraged it by asking him to dance with them. He did not, as they supposed, think that he was too old to dance : he only thought that he might not dance well and might lose his power over them. He believed that they loved him. How should they not ? Thia, though she never told him so now, loved him with her whole heart, of course, and, for all the harsh words she spoke at times, thought that no man was his equal. How should not these much gentler young women not have given their hearts to him ? He felt that he himself could love one of them, if he were not Thia's husband. They were not beautiful, as Thia was ; and they were not wise, as she was ; but he felt that if he had never seen Thia he might love one of them, or even all of them.

XX

For lack of a calendar, the homelanders had not the habit of keeping anniversaries. They never knew on what day of the year a thing had happened—did not even know that there was a year. But they knew the four seasons. They remembered that the apple-trees had been in blossom when Thol slew the dragon, and that since then the apple-trees had blossomed four times. And it seemed good to them that at the close of a day when those blossoms were again on those branches, a feast should be held in that part of the valley where the great deed had been done. Shib, who organised the feast, was anxious that it should be preceded by a hymn in praise of the slayer god. He thought this would have a good effect on the rising generation. But Thol opposed the idea, and it was dropped. Shib had also been anxious that Thia should attend the feast, sitting at Thol's right hand and signifying to the young the blessedness of the married state. Thol promised that he would beg her to come ; and he did so, as a matter of form, frequently. But Thia of course did not grace the convivial scene.

It was at a late hour of the moonlit night that Thol, flushed with adulation, withdrew from the revels, amidst entreaties that he should remain. He was still wearing the chaplet of flowers that Afa had woven for him. Afa herself was clinging to one of his arms, Moa to the other, as he went round to the eastern spur of the hill ; and Ola and Ispa and many others were footing around lightly and lingeringly, appealingly. It was rather the thought of Thia's love for him than of his for her that withheld him from kissing these attendants before he bade them good night. For his own sake he wished, as he climbed the hill, that they would not stand cooing so many farewells up to him so loudly. Thia might not understand how true he was to her. He hoped she was sleeping. But she was awake. Nor was he reassured by the laughter with which, after a moment, she greeted him. She was looking at his head. He became suddenly aware that he had not shed that chaplet. He snatched it off. She laughed the more, but with no kindness in the sound of her laughter.

' O Thia,' he said, after a search for words, ' be not wroth against those maidens ! I love none of them.'

' Is that not cruel of you, O Thol ? Do they not love you ? '

' Though they love me, O Thia, I swear to you that I love not them.'

' Why should you not ? ' she laughed. ' Are you so foolish that you think I should be sorry ? '

'O Thia,' he rebuked her, 'you speak empty words. You speak as though you did not love me.'

'I have long ceased to love you, O Thol,' she said in a low voice.

He stared at her blankly in the moonlight. His slow mind strove hard. 'But you are my wife,' he said at last. 'I am your husband. O Thia, is it indeed true that you have ceased to love me?'

'O Thol, it is most true.'

Then, by stress of the great anger that rose in him, his mind worked more quickly—or rather his tongue was loosened. He told Thia that she had never loved him. She denied this coldly. He said that she had never understood him. She denied this warmly. He reminded her that even when she was a little girl she had once called him a coward; and this too she denied; but he maintained that it was so; and she reminded him that after he had been beaten by his master for seeing the dragon he said that she too ought to have been beaten for seeing the dragon; and he denied this; but she persisted that it was so; and he then said that she ought to have been beaten; and she replied that she could be now, and she challenged him to beat her; but he did not accept her challenge; and this, she said, proved that he was a coward; and he asked her to repeat this, and she repeated it, and he then reminded her that he had slain the dragon; and she, stamping her foot, said she only wished the dragon had slain him; and she made a face at him, and rushed out of the cave, and if there had been a door she would have slammed it; and really he was quite glad that she had gone; and after she had run far she lay down upon the grass and slept till dawn, and then, rising and brushing the dew off her arms and legs, went in search of some lonely spot where she should build her a hut of clay and wattles.

And perhaps it was a sign of her alien blood that the spot chosen by her was in what we call Soho. It was the spot on which, many years later, many of my coævals were to dine in the little Restaurant du Bon-Accueil, half-way along Gerrard Street. Gone, as utterly as Thia's hut, is the dear little Restaurant du Bon-Accueil. But again I must hark back.

XXI

' Very surely,' thought Thol, some moments after the sun had waked him and shown him the empty cave and brought back last night to his memory, ' I shall find her by the pond.'

Thither, with much dignity of gait, but with the promise of forgiveness on his brow, he presently went. She was not there. There only her geese were.

These he unpenned and let go into the pond, and then, having freed his goats also, sat down and waited. He waited all day long. She did not come. Nor was she there for him in the cave when he went back to it at sunset. Neither was she at the pond next morning. Not even her geese were there now.

That she had wanted them, and not him, was a bitter thought to Thol. He had not, till now, known how much he loved her. That she had been here this morning, or in the night, made the ground somehow wonderful to him. But he frowned away from his brow the promise of forgiveness. He would not forgive Thia now. Still less would he go in quest of her. He freed his goats, guided them to some long grass and, sitting down, tried to take an intelligent interest in their doings and a lively interest in their welfare, and not wonder where Thia was.

For three whole days he tried hard—tried with all that fixity of purpose which had enabled him at last to slay the dragon. It was Afa's visit that unmanned him.

Not she nor any other of those maidens had ever come to him at the pond in Thia's time. If they happened to pass that way, they would gaze straight before them, or up at the sky, greeting neither the husband nor the wife, and simpering elaborately, as much as to say, ' We are unworthy.' But now it was straight at Thol that the approaching Afa simpered. And she said, ' I am come to be the goat-herd's help ! '

He marvelled that there was a time when he had thought he might have loved one of these maidens. He was not even sure that he knew which of them this one was. He was sure only that he despised them all. And this sentiment so contorted his mild face that there was nothing for Afa to do but toss her head and laugh and leave him.

Presently the look of great scorn in his face was succeeded by a look of even greater love. He arose and went in search of Thia. But he did not in his quest of her throw dignity to the winds. He did not ask anybody where he should find her. He walked slowly, as though bent on no errand. It was near sunset when at length he espied his lost one near to a lonely pool at the edge of the forest.

She did not see him. She sat busily plaiting wattles. There was a great pile of these beside her. And in and around the pool were her geese.

It was they that saw him first, and at sight of him they began to quack, as though in warning. Thia looked up quickly and saw Thol. He held out his arms to her, he strode towards her, calling her name ; but she was up, she was gone into the darkness of the forest.

Long he peered into that darkness, and called into it, and even groped through it, but vainly.

XXII

For people who are not accustomed to think, thought is a fatiguing affair. Thol, despite his robust body, was tired when he awoke next morning, for he had spent a great part of the night in wondering how to win back his wife to him. In the days before he slew the dragon he had been a constant thinker. Little by little he was now to regain the habit.

Step by step he reached the premiss that in order to find a means of winning Thia back he must first make clear to himself why she had ceased to love him. He put together what he could recall of the many things that in the course of time she had said in anger against him. And he came to the conclusion that he had displeased her most by dwelling so much upon his great deed. He would dwell less upon it, try even to forget it. But this would not suffice. How was she to know that he was no longer dwelling as of yore ? Perhaps he could do a second great deed ? There seemed to be none to do. He must nevertheless try to think of one—some second great deed that would much please her. It was for the homelanders' sake that the first one had found favour in her sight. And then somehow the homelanders had become less good because of it. Thia had often said so. Of course she had never blamed him for that. Still, perhaps she would not have ceased to love him if his deed had not done harm. Was there no deed by which the harm could be undone? Day by day, night by night, Thol went on thinking.

After the lapse of what we should call a week or so, he began to act also.

He knew that there could be no great thickness of barrier between the back of his cave and the back of the cave that had been the dragon's; for in his childhood he had often heard through it quite clearly the sound of the voices of Gra and her children. To make in it now a breach big enough to crawl through on hands and knees was the first step in the plan that he had formed. With a great sharp stone, hour after hour, daily, he knelt at work. Fortunately—for else must the whole plan have come to naught—the barrier was but of earth, with quite small stones in it. Nevertheless, much of strength and patience had been exerted before the first little chink of daylight met Thol's eyes.

It was a glad moment for him when, that same evening, at sunset, at last he was able to crawl through into the western cave; but as he rose and gazed around the soot-blackened lair he did not exult. His work had but begun. And his work would never end while he lived. He prayed earnestly to the sun that he might live long and always do his work rightly. Also he prayed that Thia might soon again love him.

That night, in his own cave, just as he was falling asleep, he had a doubt which greatly troubled him. He arose and went forth to a place where some ducks were. One of these he took and slew and strode away with it to the marshes. There he heaved it into the ooze. It was quickly sucked down. This was well.

On the next night he became a woodman; and many were the nights he spent in going to and fro in the dark between his cave and the nearest margin of the forest, lopping off great branches and bearing them away for storage, and even uprooting saplings and bearing away these also, and, with a flint axe, felling young trees, and chopping them into lengths that were portable. He continued this night-work until both caves were neatly stacked with wood enough to serve his purpose for a longish while.

And then—for he had thought out everything, with that thoroughness which is the virtue of slow minds—he wove two thick screens of osiers and withes, each screen rather bigger than either end of the tunnel. On the evening when the second of these was finished, he made in the dragon's cave, not far from the left-hand side of the cave's mouth, a thick knee-high heap of branches and logs, some of them dry, others green. He placed at the other side of the mouth two thick flat stones, one upon the other.

Back in his own cave, he smeared with sheep's fat a certain great stick of very dry pine-wood.

XXIII

And on the following morning history began to repeat itself. With some variations, however. For example, it was not a puny little boy but a great strong man who, as the sun rose, came rushing with every symptom of terror down the western side of the hill. And the man was not really frightened. He only seemed so.

He careered around the valley, howling now like one distraught. Responsive sheep, goats, geese, what not, made great noises of their own. From the mouths of caves and huts people darted and stood agape. Thol waved his arms wildly towards the cave upon the hill. People saw a great column of smoke climbing up from it into the sky.

'A dragon! Another dragon!' was Thol's burthen.

People gathered round him in deep wonder and agitation. He told them, in gasps, that he had come down early— very early—to look for mushrooms—and had looked back and—seen a dragon crawling up the hill. He said that he had seen it only for a moment or two: it crawled very quickly—far more quickly than the old one. He added that it was rather smaller than the old one—smaller and yet far more terrible, though its smoke was less black. Also, that it held high its head, not scorching the grass on its way.

There was no panic.

'O Thol,' said one, 'we need not fear the dragon, for here are you, to come between us and him.'

'Here by this stream,' said another, 'we shall presently bury him with great rejoicings, O high god.'

The crowd went down on its knees, thanking Thol in anticipation. But he, provident plodder, had foreseen what would happen, and had his words ready. 'Nay, O home-landers,' he said, plucking at his great beard, 'I am less young than I was. I am heavier, and not so brave. Per-adventure some younger man will dare meet this dragon for us, some day. Meanwhile, let us tempt him with the flesh of beasts, as of yore, hoping that so he will come but seldom into our midst.'

In consternation the crowd rose from its knees, and Thol walked quickly away, with a rather shambling gait.

The awful news spread apace. The valley was soon full. Long and earnestly the great throng prayed to the sun that he would call the dragon away from them. He did not so. Up, up went the steadfast smoke from within the cave. Less black it certainly was than that of the other dragon, but not less dreadful. Almost as great as the terror that it inspired was the general contempt for Thol. Many quite old men vowed to practise the needful stroke of the spear. All the youths vowed likewise—yea, and many of the maidens too. It was well-known, of course, that Thol had practised for a long while, and that any haste would be folly ; but such knowledge rather heartened than dejected the vowers. Meanwhile, the thing to do was what the craven Thol had suggested before he slunk away : to offer food as of yore. Shib, bristling with precedents, organised the labour. Thol had said that the dragon was a smaller one than the other. Perhaps therefore not so much food would be needed. But it was better to be on the safe side and offer the same ration. Up to the little shelf of ground in front of the cave's mouth were borne two goats, three ducks, two deer, three geese and two sheep.

All day long the valley was crowded with gazers, hopers, comforters of one another, offerers-up of prayers.

As day drew to its close, the tensity increased. Would this dragon wake and eat at sunset, as that other had been wont to do ? How soon would appear through the smoke that glimpse of nether fire which proclaimed that his head was out of the cave, alert and active ? And would that glow rise and fall, in the old way, twelve times, with the sound of the clashed jaws? What was in store for the homeland to-night?

None but Thol knew.

XXIV

He, very wisely, had rested all day in preparation for the tasks of evening and night. Two or three times, moving aside the screen that kept the smoke out of his cave, he had crawled through the opening and, drawing the other screen across the other side of it, had tended the fire. For the rest, he had been all inactive.

As twilight crept into the cave, he knelt in solemn supplication to the departing sun. Presently, when darkness had descended, he struck two flints, lit one end of his pine-wood staff, moved the screen aside, drew a long deep breath, and crawled swiftly into the other cave. Slowly he moved his torch from side to side of the cave's mouth, along the ground. He was holding it in his left hand, and in his right hand was holding one of the two flat stones. After a pause, still kneeling, he raised high the torch for a moment or two and then sharply lowered it in the direction of one of the smoke-clouded animals. At the same time he powerfully clashed the one stone down upon the other. Another pause, and he repeated these actions exactly, directing the torch towards the next animal. He performed them ten times in all. Then he extinguished his torch and crept quickly home, puffing and spluttering and snorting, glad to escape into clear air.

When he had regained his breath, he crawled back to drag the carcasses in. The roe and the buck he left where

63

they were. He had calculated that three nightly journeys to the marshes and back would be all that he could achieve. First he would take the two sheep, one on each shoulder ; next, the goats ; lastly the birds, three necks in either hand. The buck and the roe would be too heavy to be carried together, and for five journeys there would certainly not be time. It was for this reason that he had described the dragon as smaller than the old one, and had clashed the stones ten times only.

From the valley rose sounds of rejoicing that all was well for the homeland to-night. One by one, Thol transferred the carcasses to his own cave. He waited there among them till the dead of night, when all folk would be sleeping. Then, shouldering the two sheep, he sallied forth down the hill and away to the marshes.

He accomplished the whole of his night-work before the stars had begun to fade. Then, having replenished and banked the fire, he lay down to sleep. Some four hours later he woke to go and tend the fire again, and then again slept.

XXV

It was a toilsome, lonesome, monotonous and fuliginous life that Thol had chosen ; but he never faltered in it. Always at night-fall he impersonated the dragon, and in the small hours went his journeys to the marshes ; and never once did he let the fire die.

The afternoons passed very slowly. He wished he could sally forth into the sunshine, like other men. He paced round and round his cave, hour after hour, a strange figure, dark-handed, dark-visaged, dark-bearded.

In so far as they deigned to remember him at all, the homelanders supposed he had gone away, that first morning, across the waters or through the forests, to some land where he could look men in the face.

Here he was, however, in their midst, a strenuous and faithful servant.

He had a stern grim joy in the hardness of his life—save that he could never ask Thia to share it with him. He had not foreseen—it was the one thing he had not thought out well—how hard the life would be. The great deed by which he had thought to bring Thia back to him must forever keep them asunder. Thus he had done an even greater deed than he intended. And his stern grim joy in it was thereby the greater.

XXVI

Had she so wished, Thia might have become very popular and have regained something of her past glory. After Thol's confession of cowardice she had instantly risen in the homelanders' esteem. How very right she had been to leave him! Friendly eyes and friendly words greeted her. But when they all knelt praying the sun to call the dragon away, she remained upright and mute. And after-wards, when she was asked why, she said that it was well that the dragon should abide among them, for thus would they all be the better, in heart and deed, and therefore truly the happier, could they but know it. She said that whether or not they could know it, so it was.

These sayings of hers were taken in bad part, and she was shunned because of them. This did not mar the joy she had in knowing that all was well once more in the homeland.

She felt herself not at all unblest in the quiet spinsterly life she was leading, in and out of her trim new hut, with her dear flock of geese about her.

Of Thol, nowadays, she thought more gently. She felt that if he had stayed in the homeland she would have gone back to him. It would have been her bounden duty to be with him and to comfort him in his shame. Indeed his shame made him dear to her once more. As the days passed she thought more and more about him. It was strange that he had gone from the homeland. No home-lander ever had gone forth into the perils of the lands beyond. If she herself, daughter of wanderers, had roved away instead of building this hut to dwell in, she might not have much marvelled at herself, less brave though she was than Thol. And Thol was no longer brave. How had he, fearing a dragon smaller than that other, conquered his fear of known and unknown things that were worse yet, far worse yet?

And one evening a strange doubt came to her. Might it not be that Thol was still in the homeland? In one of all these dark forests he might be living, with nuts and berries to support life. Or, she further guessed, he might even be in his own cave, stealing out at night when all but the watchmen on the other side of the hill were sleeping. This notion, foolish though it seemed to her, possessed her mind.

So soon as silence and sleep had descended on the home-land, Thia herself stole out into the clear starlit night. Not far from the eastern spur of the hill she lay down in a clump of long grass, and thence, gazing up, watched the cave's mouth steadily.

XXVII

Some one presently came forth : and yes, it was Thol. Slowly he came down the hill, with his head bent forward, with his hands up to his bowed shoulders, and two burdens at his back—two goats, as Thia saw when presently Thol turned aside southward. He looked very strange. His hair and face seemed to have grown quite dark. And what was he doing with those two goats ? Thia lay still, with a fast-beating heart. She felt that her voice would not have come, even had she tried to call to him.

She watched him out of sight, then rose to her feet and, hesitatingly, went to the foot of the hill, and then, quickly and resolutely, went up it and into the cave.

Quick-witted though she was, the sight of three geese and three ducks and of two sheep puzzled her deeply ; and not less did she wonder at the quantity of stacked wood. And what was that fence of osiers against the wall ? She moved it slightly and saw a great breach in the wall ; and through this some smoke came drifting in. And now her quick wits began to work—but in such wise as to make her bewilderment the deeper.

Suddenly, drawing a deep breath, she went down on her hands and knees, and crawled, quick as a serpent, through the smoke.

She was soon back again. Blinking hard and shaking the smoke from her nostrils, she went to breathe the clear air at the cave's mouth. But, good though this air was, she hardly tasted it. She had burst out sobbing. She, who never in all her life had shed tears, sobbed much now. But she remembered that tears make people's eyes ugly.

So she controlled herself and dried her eyes vigorously. She had not remembered that the palms of her hands must be all black from her crawl. When she saw them, and knew what her face must be now, she burst out laughing. And the sound made her feel very young, for it was long since she had laughed. But, as she wished to please Thol's eyes, she retired to the back of the cave and crouched where she would scarcely be seen by him when he came.

He came at last, and then, very softly, she cried out to him, ' Thol ! '

He, brave though he was, started violently.

' Do not look at me, O Thol ! Not yet ! For my face is black and would displease you. Look at me only after you have heard me. O Thol, if they said now that you were a god, almost would I believe them. But if you were a god your deed would be less great. The wonder is that you are a man, and were once mine. O Thol, forgive me, keep me here with you, need me ! '

But he slowly answered, ' Nay, O Thia, this cave is not now for a woman.'

' Not for a woman that is your wife and lover ? Think ! Was it not for my sake and for love of me that you thought to do what you are doing ? '

' Yea, O Thia. Yet, now that I am doing it, itself suffices me. I am strong, and suffer not under the burden of it. The very heaviness of it makes me glad. And now your knowledge of it gladdens me, too. But I would not have you bear the least part of it with me. Go to your own home ! '

' You speak firmly, O great dragon ! Yet will not I obey you. Tell me of your work. Is it to the marshes that you take the beasts and the birds ? '

'Yea. Begone, small dear one!' And he stooped down to take the two sheep.

'Once, long ago, you wished that a lad might help you in your hard work. O Thol, I am as I was, trustier than any lad. It were better that you should go twice, not thrice, every night, to the marshes. I will always take the birds.' And she rose to take them.

But a thought came to her, giving her pause. And she said, 'The fire must first be tended.'

'It has no need yet,' he answered. 'I tend it when I come back from the last journey.'

'To-night it shall be tended earlier. And I will so tend it that it shall last long.' She was down on her knees and off into the smoke before he could stop her. He followed her, protesting that such work was not for her. She did it, nevertheless, very well. And presently, side by side, he with two sheep, she with three birds' necks in either fist, they went forth into the starlight, and down away to the marshes.

There, having duly sunk their burdens, they took each other by the hand, and turned homeward. At one of the running brooks on their way home, Thia halted. 'Here,' she said, 'will I wash myself well. And do you too, O Thol, so that when we wake in the morning my face shall not displease you.'

XXVIII

Every night Thia accompanied Thol on one of the two journeys; and during the other she would go to the forest and gather wood, so that there should always be plenty of fuel in hand. She was sorry to have had to abandon her geese, for she felt they would not be as happy with any one as they had been with her. Nothing else whatever was there to mar her joy in the life that she and Thol were leading together, and in the good that they were doing. It amused her to know that the homelanders would think she had wandered away—she who was serving them so well. Its very secrecy made her life the more joyous.

Daily she prayed to the sun and other gods that she and Thol might live to be very old and might never fail in their work.

But the sun and those others were not good listeners.

As the nights lengthened and the leaves began to fall, the mists over the marshes and around them grew ever thicker. It was not easy to find the way through them ; and they were very cold, and had a savour that was bitter to the tongue and to the nostrils. And one morning Thia, when she woke, was shivering from head to foot, though she was in Thol's arms. She slipped away from him without waking him, and went not merely to tend the fire but also to warm herself at it. All through the morning she was shivering ; and in the evening her hands became hot, as did her face and all her body. She felt very weak. She could laugh no more now at Thol's disquietude. She lay down, but could not lie very still. At about the time when they were wont to sally forth, she rose up, feeling that even though she might not be able to carry the birds to-night the journey would freshen her. She soon found that she was too weak even to stand. Thol was very loth to leave her ; but she insisted that the work must be done. Again and again, next day and during the next night, she implored him that if she died he would not mourn her

70

very much and would not once falter in the work. He promised that he would not falter. Other days and nights passed. It seemed to Thol that Thia had ceased to know him. She did not even follow him with her eyes now. One morning, at daybreak, soon after his return from the third journey, she seemed, by her gaze, to know him. But presently she died in his arms.

On that night he went to the forest and dug a grave for his wife. Then, returning to the cave, he took her in his arms for the last time, and carried her away, and buried her.

In the time that followed, he was not altogether lonely. He felt by day that somehow she was in the cave with him still, and by night he felt that she walked with him. He never faltered in the work.

He faltered not much even when the marshes did to him as they had done to Thia. Shivering in every limb, or hot and aching, and very weak, he yet forced himself to tend the fire and at nightfall to brandish the torch and clash the stones and drag in the beasts and birds. It irked him that he was not strong enough to carry even one sheep away. Surely he would be strong again soon? For Thia's sake, and for the homeland's, he wished ardently to live. But there came an evening when the watchers in the valley saw no rising and falling, heard no clashing, of the dragon's jaws.

XXIX

Would the dragon come forth to-night? The valley on the further side of the stream was now thickly crowded. On the nearer side were many single adventurers, with spears. Their prowess and skill were not tested. The dragon came not forth.

In the dawn it was noted that his smoke was far less thick than it was wont to be. Soon it ceased altogether. What had happened? Perchance the dragon was ailing? But even an ailing dragon would breathe. A great glad surmise tremulously formed itself. Was the dragon dead?

The surmise quickly became a firm belief—so firm that, in spite of protests from the precise Shib, songs of thanksgiving were heartily sung before the cave was approached and examined.

People were much puzzled. The dead man lying at the cave's mouth, grasping in one hand a flat stone and in the other a charred staff, was not instantly recognised as Thol, so black were his hair and skin; nor was he instantly recognised as the dragon. The quantities of stacked wood, the tunnel into the cave where Thol had lived, did not quickly divulge their meaning. Only after long arguments and many conjectures did the homelanders understand the trick that had been played on them. Why, with what evil intent, it had been played, they were almost too angry to discuss at present. But certain words of Thia's were remembered; and it was felt that she herself perhaps had put the trick into Thol's mind and that this was why she had fled the homeland. She had better not set foot in it again.

Before the sun sank, Thol was buried without honour, and far from Thia.

And before the sun sank many other times the homelanders were as they had been before the coming of the true dragon, and as they had been again before the false one was among them.

FINIS

And thus—does our tale end unhappily? I think not. After all, the homelanders at large are rather shadowy to us. Oc and Loga, Shib and Veo, Afa and her like, and all those others, all those nameless others, do not mean much to us. It is Thol and Thia that we care about. For their sake we wish that the good they did could have been lasting. But it is not in the nature of things that anything —except the nature of things—should last. Saints and wise statesmen can do much. Their reward is in the doing of it. They are lucky if they do not live long enough to see the undoing. It should suffice us that Thol and Thia together in their last days knew a happiness greater than they had ever known—Thol a greater happiness than in the days of his glory, and Thia than in the days of hers.

F

THE GUERDON

THE GUERDON

THAT it hardly was, that it all bleakly and unbeguilingly *wasn't* for ' the likes ' of *him*—poor decent Stamfordham —to rap out queries about the owner of the to him unknown and unsuggestive name that had, in these days, been thrust on him with such a wealth of commendatory gesture, was precisely what now, as he took, with his prepared list of New Year *colifichets* and whatever, his way to the great gaudy palace, fairly flicked his cheek with the sense of his having never before so let himself in, as he ruefully phrased it, without letting anything, by the same token, out.

' Anything ' was, after all, only another name for *the* thing. But he was to ask himself what earthly good it was, anyhow, to have kept in its confinement the furred and clawed, the bristling and now all but audibly scratching domestic pet, if he himself had to be figured as bearing it company inside the bag. There wasn't, he felt himself blindly protesting, room in there for the two of them ; and the imminent addition of a Personage fairly caused our friend to bristle in the manner of the imagined captive that had till now symbolised well enough for him his whole dim bland ignorance of the matter in hand. Hadn't he all the time been reckoning precisely *without* that Personage —*without* the greater dimness that was to be expected of *him*—without, above all, that dreadful lesser blandness in virtue of which such Personages tend to come down on you, as it were, straight, with demands for side-lights? There wasn't a 'bally' glimmer of a side-light, heaven help him, that he could throw. He hadn't the beginning of a notion—since it had been a point of pride with him, as well as of urbanity, not to ask—who the fellow, the so presumably illustrious and deserving chap in question *was*. This omission so loomed for him that he was to be conscious, as he came to the end of the great moist avenue, of a felt doubt as to whether he could, in his bemusement, now 'place' anybody at all; to which condition of his may have been due the impulse that, at the reached gates of the palace, caused him to pause and all vaguely, all peeringly inquire of one of the sentries: 'To whom do you beautifully belong?'

The question, however, was to answer itself, then and there, to the effect that this functionary belonged to whom *he* belonged to; and the converse of this reminder, presenting itself simultaneously to his consciousness, was to make him feel when he was a few minutes later ushered into the Presence, that he had never so intensely, for general abjectness and sheer situational funk, belonged as now. He caught himself wondering whether, on this basis, he were even animate, so strong was his sense of being a 'bit' of the furniture of the great glossy 'study'—of being some oiled and ever so handy object moving smoothly on castors, or revolving, at the touch of a small red royal finger, on a pivot. It would be placed questioningly, that finger—and his prevision held him as with the long-drawn pang of nightmare—on the cryptic name. That it occurred, this name, almost at the very end of the interminable list, figured to him not as a respite but as a prolongment of the perspirational agony. So that when, at long last, that finger *was* placed, with a roll towards him of the blue, the prominent family eye of the seated reader, it was with a groan of something like relief that he faintly uttered an ' Oh well, Sir, he *is*, you know—and with all submission, hang it, just *isn't* he though?—of an eminence ! '

It was in the silence following this fling that there budded for him the wild, the all but unlooked-for hope that ' What *sort*, my dear man, of eminence? ' was a question not, possibly, going to be asked at all. It fairly burst for him and blossomed, this bud, as the royal eye rolled away from his into space. It never, till beautifully now, had struck our poor harassed friend that his master might, in some sort, be prey to those very, those inhibitive delicacies that had played, from first to last, so eminently the deuce with *him*. He was to see, a moment later, that the royal eye had poised—had, from its slow flight around the mouldings of the florid Hanoverian ceiling, positively swooped—on the fat scarlet book of reference which, fraught with a title that was a very beam of the catchy and the chatty, lay beside the blotting-pad. The royal eye rested, the royal eye even dilated, to such an extent that Stamfordham had anticipatively the sense of being commanded to turn for a few minutes his back, and of overhearing in that interval the rustle of the turned leaves.

That no such command came, that there *was* no recourse to the dreadful volume, somewhat confirmed for him his made guess that on the great grey beach of the hesitational and renunciational he was not—or wasn't all deniably not —the only pebble. For an instant, nevertheless, during which the prominent blue eye rested on a prominent blue pencil, it seemed that this guess might be, by an immense *coup de roi,* terrifically shattered. Our friend held, as for an eternity, his breath. He was to form, in later years, a theory that the name really *had* stood in peril of deletion, and that what saved it was that the good little man, as doing, under the glare shed by his predecessors, the great dynastic ' job ' in a land that had been under two Jameses and no less than eight Henrys, had all humbly and meltingly resolved to ' let it go at that.'

T. FENNING DODWORTH

T. FENNING DODWORTH

1922.

This name is seldom, if ever, on the lips of the man in the street. But it is a name highly esteemed by men whose good opinion is most worth having. When the idols of our market-place shall have been jerked from their pedestals by irreverent Time, Fenning Dodworth will not be utterly forgotten. His name will crop up *passim*, and honourably, in the pages of whatever Grevilles and Creeveys we have had among us during the past thirty years.—' Met Fenning Dodworth in Pall Mall this morning. He told me he had it on the best authority that St. John Brodrick would not be put up to speak on the Second Reading.'—' Heard an amusing and characteristic *mot* of Fenning Dodworth's. He was dining with some other men at E. Beckett's one night last week, when the conversation turned on Winston's speech at Oldham. Beckett said, " Whatever Winston's faults may be, he has genius." " That," said Dodworth, in the silence that ensued, " is a proposition on which I should like to meditate before endorsing it." Collapse of Beckett ! '—' Sat next to Dodworth at the Cordwainers' dinner. He said that he did not at all like the look of things in the Far East. Later in the evening I asked him point-blank whether the phrase " A Government of Pecksniffs," which has been going the rounds, had been coined by him. " It may have been," he said drily. Characteristic ! '

Dodworth's wit is undeniable. It is not, certainly, of the kind that I like best and rate highest—the kind that pierces without leaving a wound. Dodworth's shafts are barbed, and, though it were too much to say that they are poisoned, assuredly they have been dipped in very caustic acids. And he has not humour. At least, if he has, he uses it sparingly, and never at all in my presence. But humour, delightful though it is for current purposes, lacks durability. There are fashions in humour, and they are always changing. Wit, on the other hand, being a hard and clean-cut thing, is always as good as new. Dodworth's gems, set in the golden tissue of private journals given to the world, will have lost nothing of their flash. And among readers of those journals there will be a great desire to know what Dodworth himself was like. Keepers of journals are so apt to omit that sort of thing. What faces, complexions, girths, heights, gaits, voices, gestures, tricks of manner, shirt-studs, preferences in food and wine, had the more or less eminent men who were forever pouring into the diarist's ear their hopeful or fearful conjectures about to-morrow night's Division? The diarist knew, and had therefore no need to tell himself. But *we* don't know, and we want to know. That Division was a turning-point in the world's history? No doubt. Those more or less eminent men are dust? Alas, yes. But they were flesh and blood to the diarist, and he could have made them so to us, too. It may be that the diarists of our own day have held in mind the omissions of their forerunners, and make a point of telling themselves just the things that are a matter of course to them. But it may be otherwise. So I insert here, for posterity, a note or two on the surface of Fenning Dodworth—who, quite apart from his wit, seems to me one of the most remarkable, the strongest and, in a way, most successful men of our time.

Dignity, a Roman dignity, is the keynote of his appearance. This is undoubtedly one of the causes of his success. Is it also, I sometimes ask myself, partly a result of his success? But no. Twenty years ago (when first I made his acquaintance) he was as impressive as he is, at the age of sixty, now. Moreover, had his mind any knack to remould his body, surely he would be taller. He remains very far below the middle height. But he carries his head high, thus envisaging the more easily the ruck of common objects, and making on such of those objects as are animate the kind of effect which his unaided stature might preclude. One of his eyebrows is slightly raised ; the other is slightly lowered, to hold in position a black-rimmed single eyeglass. His nose is magnificently Roman. His lips are small, firm, admirably chiselled, and every word that falls from them is very precisely articulated. His chin is very strong, and his chest (in proportion to his height) deep. He has the neatest of hands and feet. Draped in a toga, and without his monocle, he might pass for a statuette of Seneca. But he prefers and affects a more recent style of costume—the style, somewhat, of the Victorian statesmen who flourished in his youth : a frock-coat and a rather large top-hat, a collar well-open at the throat, and round it a riband of black silk tied in a loose bow. He is a good judge (and, I take it, the sole survivor among judges) of sherry. Nor is this the only way in which he imparts agreeably the flavour of a past age. In Thackeray, in Trollope, in the old volumes of *Punch*, you will have found a wealth of testimony to the fact that persons of high importance, meeting persons of slight importance, often did not shake hands, but offered a finger or two to be shaken. Incredible, nevertheless? Then perhaps you will not believe me when I say that I have been offered two fingers by Dodworth. Indignantly you ask whether I shook them. I avoid your eye, I evade your question, I do but say that I am very susceptible to—well, to greatness.

The proof, for me, of Dodworth's greatness is in what he has achieved. He has made so much out of so little. Many men have been ten times more successful (in the coarse sense of that word) without winning a tithe of what he has won. It is often said that nothing succeeds like success. Dodworth's career offers a corrective of such cynicism—or would do so if his case were a common one. I admit that to have excelled in some undertaking is not always needed for the making of a great prestige. Dukes and princes are not without honour even if they have done nothing—or even if they shall have tried to do something and failed. Dodworth was not born exempt from the advisability of doing something. ' b. 12. Feb. 1860, o.s. of J. Dodworth and Rachel, e.d. of W. K. Fenning, of Norwich.' Thus does he speak, in *Who's Who*, of his origin ; and as he is (albeit less a toady than any man I know) one of the most finished snobs I have ever met, his reticence tells much. Old Mr. Dodworth was of some town so mean that it is not mentionable. And what did he do there? What, for that matter, did old Mr. Fenning do at Norwich? Something dreadful, you may be sure, from the social standpoint. What school was the young Dodworth sent to? Obviously to some school, else we should find ' *Educ. :* privately.' There is no mention of any school. The boy went to some school that is unmentionable. But it may be surmised that he did well there, for we do find ' *Educ. :* Won open scholarship at Queen's Coll., Oxford, 1879.' A presage, this, of coarse successes. But mark the sequel ! ' Second Class in Classical Mods., 1881 ; Third Class, Lit. Hum., 1883. Treasurer of Union, 1882.' He was thrice a candidate for the Presidency of the Union ; and I happen to have met in later years two of his successful opponents, both of them men rather prominent in public life to-day. One of them told me that Dodworth's speeches were the wittiest ever heard in the Union ' or, I do believe, anywhere else ' ; the other described them as the most closely reasoned. And neither of these men spoke of Fenning Dodworth as one who had not lived up to his early promise. They seemed to pride themselves, rather, on having always foreseen his ascendancy.

Men prominent in public life are mostly hard to converse with. They lack small-talk, and at the same time one doesn't like to confront them with their own great themes. I have found that the best way to put them at their ease, to make them expand and glow, is to mention Fenning Dodworth. They are all, from their various standpoints, of one mind about him. Judges think he would have been an ornament to the Bench, statesmen wish he were in the Cabinet, diplomatists wish he were one of them, and wish he could be at Tokyo or Pekin or wherever at the moment his grasp of things in the Far East and his unfailing dislike of the look of them would be most obviously invaluable. And all these gods console themselves with anecdotes of his wit—some mordant thing he said years ago, some equally mordant thing he said last week. ' I remember,' a Judge will tell you, ' one night at mess on the Northern Circuit, somebody said " I call Bosanquet a very strong man in Nisi Prius." Dodworth looked at him in that queer dry way of his, and said " Ah ! I should hardly go so far as that." ' The Judge will then throw himself back in his chair and alarm you with symptoms of choking. If you ask him why Dodworth did not remain at the Bar, the answer will be that he got so few briefs : ' He was the best all-round Junior I ever heard, but he wasn't a man for the jury : you can't saw a plank of wood with a razor. Pity he didn't practise in Chancery ! But I suppose he was right to devote himself to politics. He's had more scope there.'

He has not, certainly, been cramped. For him there has been no durance within the four walls of the House of Commons. He contested (I quote again his narrative in *Who's Who*) ' East Grinstead, 1888 ; Dulwich, 1890 ; Skipton, 1891 ; Cannock, 1893 ; Haggerston, 1897 ; Pontypool, 1898 ; Peebles, 1900.' He escaped, every time, the evils of election. (And his good angel stood not less close to him on the three occasions when he offered himself as candidate for the London County Council.) Voters, like jurors, would not rise to him. At length it was borne in even on the leaders of his Party that they must after all be content to rely on his pen rather than on his tongue. ' Has been,' he says in *Who's Who*, ' for many years a contributor to the leading reviews.' That is so. Those reviews are not edited by the vulgar. Dodworth's MSS. have always been printed. I used to read articles by him when I was yet a schoolboy, and to wonder whether the Liberal Party would ever again hold up its hideous head. I remember one entitled ' The Franchise Bill— And After,' and another entitled ' The Home Rule Peril —And After.' Both seemed to me splendid, partly perhaps because of their titles. Dodworth was, I believe, the first publicist to use that magical affix, that somehow statesman-like, mysterious, intriguing formula, ' —And After.' In later years I began to think him narrow in his views. I became a prey to that sentimentalism from which in one's schooldays one is immune, and ceased to regard the ideas of the Liberal Party as perverse. Dodworth as a political thinker seemed to me lacking in generosity, lacking even (despite his invariable ' —And After ') in foresight. But the older I grew, and the less capable of his doctrine, the more surely did I appreciate his command of literary form. Losing the taste which undergraduates have for conceits and florid graces, I rendered justice to the sombre astrin-gency of Dodworth's prose. Whatever his theme, what-ever the Liberal Party was in office proposing, or in opposition opposing, his article was substantially the same as every other article he had written ; but, like some masterpiece in music, it never palled. With perfect sobriety and fairness he would state the arguments on which the Liberal spokesmen had been basing their case ; he would make these *seem* quite unanswerable ; but then, suddenly, like a panther crouching to spring, he would pause, he would begin a new paragraph : What are the facts ? The panther had sprung. It was always a great moment. I usually skipped the forthcoming facts and went on to the point where Dodworth worked back to first principles and historic parallels and (best of all) quotations from the mighty dead. He was always very adept in what may be called the suspensive method of quotation. ' It was written long ago, by one who saw further and grasped more firmly than is given to most men to see and to grasp, that " the fate of nations is in the conscience of their rulers." It is for us to ask ourselves whether, in saying this, Mr. Burke was right.' Or, ' In a speech delivered in the Guildhall at a time when Europe stood in the shadow of great events, a First Minister of the Crown, as to whom not a few of us are agreed in wishing that he were alive to-day, said that the art of government lay in the construction of safeguards. Mr. Disraeli never spoke a truer word.' But presently, with a swoop from the past to the present, and from the general to the particular, the scholar would be merged in the panther, and the Liberal Party be mauled so frightfully that at last even the panther seemed to recoil in pity for ' a Party once great ' and to wonder if some excuse could not be found for it. The excuse, the last sentence of Dodworth's article, was usually *Quos deus vult perdere prius dementat*; but sometimes, more simply and poignantly, *Quos deus vult.*

Fifteen years ago it seemed to the leaders of his Party and to the veiled prophets in their Central Office, that such a voice as his, if it were heard daily by a vast public, would be proportionately more potent than in its monthly addresses to the few. There was an old-established daily newspaper whose proprietor had just died, and his estate not yet been wound up. And there was, on one of the back benches of the Party, a stout, silent man, middle-aged, very affluent, a Mister. Some word in season, some word in the ear, was spoken to this man, on a moonless night, by one of the veiled prophets. That old-established newspaper was acquired. Dodworth was installed in the editorial chair, gave the keynote to the staff, and wrote every night a leading article with his own incisive pen. But ' you cannot,' as the Judge said, ' saw a plank of wood with a razor.' To uneducated readers the almost-daily-recurring

phrase *Quos deus vult* had no meaning. Half-educated
readers thought it meant ' The Lord watch between thee
and me when we are absent one from another.' The
circulation fell by leaps and bounds. Advertisers withdrew
their advertisements. Within six months (for the proprietor
was now a Sir, and oafishly did not want to become something better) that old-established newspaper ceased utterly
to be. ' This,' I thought, ' really *is* a set-back for Dodworth.'
I was far from right. The set-back was rather for myself.
I received no payment for three or four of the book-reviews
that I had contributed, and I paid two guineas for my share
of the dinner offered to Dodworth at the Savoy Hotel, and
five guineas towards a portrait of him ' in oils ' by one of
the oldest and worst of Royal Academicians. This portrait
was presented to him after dinner by our chairman (the
Prime Minister of that time) in a speech that would have
been cloying if it had been more fluent. Dodworth
bandied no compliments. This was a private occasion, and
he lived up to his reputation of being privately as caustic
about his friends as he was publicly about his foes. He
' twitted ' his friend the Prime Minister with one thing
and another, reducing that statesman and the whole
company to paroxysms of appreciation. . . . ' Our chairman has said that he will continue to do what in him lies
to help the cause that we all have at heart (hear, hear).
Well, wherever there is a cause there is also an effect
(laughter). I hope that the effect in this instance will be
of the kind that we all desiderate (much laughter). I do
not say that it will be, I only say I hope that it will be
(hysterics).' I wish I could recall more of what Dodworth
said. Every one agreed that he was in his best vein and
had never been more pungent.

Two or three years later I attended another banquet at which he was the guest of the evening—a banquet at the Hotel Cecil, offered by the Playgoers' Club. He had written a three-act comedy : ' THE ANTAGONISTS—A Satire on Certain Aspects of Political Life.' This had been instantly snapped up, and soon produced, with a very strong cast, by Sir George Alexander. All the leaders of both parties in both Houses were present on the first night, and many of them (rashly, so weak were they with laughter) were present also on the second, third and fourth nights, and would probably have been present on other nights, too ; but (such was the absenteeism of the vulgar) there were no other nights. Dodworth had again not sawn the plank. But it was clear to me, a week later, on the Sunday evening fixed—some time previously—for the banquet, that the edge of his razor was quite unblunted. In responding to the speech of the President (who had said nothing to imply that the play was not still running), Dodworth taunted us, very tartly, with our failure to arrest the decay of dramatic art by elevating the taste of the public. Had he been less witty, he might rather have spoilt our evening, so deep did he plant in us a sense of our failure. His own peculiar strength was never better attested than when, later in the evening, Alexander rose and announced with pride that he had that morning secured from his friend Fenning Dodworth the promise to write another comedy for the St. James's Theatre.

As this was never performed, I am quite sure it was never written. And I think the cause of the unfulfilment is to be found in the history of our time. Politics had now become too tense and terrible for the lighter use of Dodworth's pen. After the death of Sir Henry Campbell-

Bannerman ' a Party once great ' cast off what old remnants of decency had clung to it. Mr. Lloyd George composed a Budget. The Lords rejected it. Mr. Asquith introduced the Parliament Bill. Those were stirring times ; and during them, as it seemed to me, Dodworth was greater, aye ! and happier, than he had ever been. Constitutional points and precedents had always lain very near to his heart. In them he had always both publicly and privately abounded. His dislike of the look of things in the Far East had never been more than skin-deep. Such themes as the Reform Bill of 1832 had ever touched him to far finer issues. The fiscal problems raised by Mr. Chamberlain, strongly though he had backed Mr. Chamberlain's solution of them, had left in abeyance what was best in him. The desirability of enriching some rich manufacturers cannot be expressed in the grand manner. Mr. Asquith's desire to limit the Lords' veto was a worthy theme. Month followed month. I soon lost count of Dodworth's articles. ' The Assault on the Constitution— And After,' ' The Betrayal—And After,' ' The End of All Things—And After,' are the only three that I recall. Enough that he was at his best in all of them, and ended every one of them with the inference that Mr. Asquith (one of his staunchest though most reluctant admirers) was mad.

I had the good fortune to meet him constantly in those days of crisis. I hardly know how this was. I did not seek him out. It seemed simply that he had become ubiquitous. Maybe his zest had multiplied him by 100 or so, enabling him to be in as many places at once. He looked younger. He talked more quickly than was his wont, though with an elocution as impeccable as ever. He had none of those austere, prim silences for which he was so feared. He was a bard. His command of the nobler, the statesmanlike kind of slang, and his unction in the use of it, had never been so mesmeric. ' If the Sovereign sent for the P. M. and said " I shall do nothing till the case arises ", what could the P. M. say? Nothing. On the other hand, if the P. M. sought audience to-morrow *with a view to a contingent assurance*, and the Sovereign said " That's all very well, but what d'you hypothecate?" and the P. M. simply referred him back to what Mr. G. said when The Buffalo was threatening to throw out the Franchise of '85—*then* what? The Sovereign would be in a damned ticklish position. And the only way out of it ', etc. Little wonder that agéd ears played truant at his tales, and younger hearings were quite ravishéd, so sweet and voluble was his discourse.

Alas, the Sovereign did not slip through whatever loophole it was that Dodworth descried. The P. M. did not climb down. The Buffalo did not rise from the grave. Lord L. sold the pass. The backwoodsmen went back to the backwoods. Dodworth was left sitting among the ruins of the Constitution. But the position suited him. He was still in his element, and great. It was at the outbreak of the War that I feared there might be no more of him. And there was, indeed, less. No longer young, he did not acquire more than a smattering of the military idiom, nor any complete grasp of strategy. But he was ever in close touch with the War Office and with G.H.Q., and was still fairly oracular. Several times in the last year of the conflict, he visited (with temporary rank of Lieutenant-Colonel) certain sectors of the Western Front and made speeches to the men in the trenches, declaring himself well-satisfied with their *morale,* and being very caustic about the enemy ; but it may be doubted whether he, whose spell had never worked on the man in the street, was fully relished by the men in the trenches. *Non omni omnia.* Colonel Dodworth was formed for successes of the more exquisite kind. I think the Ministry of Information erred in supposing that his article, ' Pax Britannica—And After,' would be of immense use all the world over. But the error was a generous one. The article was translated into thirty-seven foreign languages and fifty-eight foreign dialects. Twelve million copies of it were printed on hand-woven paper, and these were despatched in a series of special trains to a southern port. The Admiralty, at the last moment, could not supply transport for them, and the local authorities complained of them that they blocked the dock. The matter was referred to the Ministry of Reconstruction, which purchased a wheat-field twenty miles inland and erected on it a large shed of concrete and steel for the reception of Dodworth's pamphlets, pending distribution. This shed was nearly finished at the moment when the Armistice was signed, and it was finished soon after. Whether the pamphlets are in it, or just where they are, I do not know. Blame whom you will. I care not. Dodworth had even in the War another of his exquisite successes.

Yet I am glad for him that we have Peace. At first I was afraid it might be bad for him. We had been promised a new world ; and to that, though he had come so well through the War, I feared he would not be able to adjust himself. The new world was to be, in many respects, rather dreadful—a benign cataclysm, but still a cataclysm, and Dodworth perhaps not to be found in any of his favourite chairs when the crystal waters subsided and the smiling land was revealed. We may have it yet. But the danger seems to be less imminent. A few days ago I met Dodworth in Bird-Cage Walk, and said to him something about it seeming likely that moderate councils would prevail among the Labour men. 'Ah,' he said in that queer dry way of his, 'it's their moderate intelligence that's the danger.' He said it instantly (and it was obviously not a thing he could have prepared). And the very fact that he was able to jest once more was a heartening proof for me of his belief that the worst was past. Another good sign was that he had resumed his top-hat. During the last eighteen months of the War he had worn a thing of soft black felt, which I took to be a symbol of inward pessimism ; and he had gone on wearing this long after the treaty of Peace was signed—a retention which seemed to me equally sinister, as a silent manifesto of unfaith in the future of our body politic. But now he was crowned once more with a cylinder from his old Victorian block. And a further good sign was that he was on his way to the House. In the old days, he had been wont to occupy, whenever an important debate was afoot, one or another of those nice seats near the Serjeant-at-Arms. In the course of the War he had ceased from such attendance. He had become very bitter against 'the politicians' and especially 'the lawyer politicians.' But I suspect that what revolted him even more was the sight of the new, the 'business' types on the Treasury Bench—the bullet-headed men in reefer-jackets, rising to tell the House what they were 'out for' and what they were 'up against,' and why they had 'pushed' this and 'turned down' that, and forgetting to address the Chair. Dodworth's return to St. Stephen's implied for me the obsolescence of such men. I asked him what he thought, from a tactical standpoint, of the line recently taken by the Independent Liberals. ' I am afraid,' he said, ' there is not much hope for these Adullamites without a Cave.' This phrase he may not have coined on the spur of the moment. But, even so, how extraordinarily good ! It's wicked, it's unjust, it hurts, but—it seems to me even more delicious than his description of Gladstone in '86 as ' a Moses without a Pisgah.' I think he was pleased, in his queer dry way, by my delight, for he said he would send me a copy of his forthcoming book—a selection from the political articles written by him since his earliest days. He had not, he said (quoting, I think, from his preface), intended to resuscitate these ephemeræ. The idea was not his but ——'s (he named the head of an historic firm of publishers). The book will be out next month, and will include that most recent of his articles, ' A Short Shrift for Sinn Fein— And After.' It will be ' remaindered,' of course, in a year or so, but will meanwhile have taken an honoured place in every eminent man's library. By the way, I had feared that Mr. Lloyd George, with his Celtic rather than classic mind, made a break in the long line of Prime Ministers who have rated Dodworth highly. I am glad to hear that at a dinner held somewhere the night before last he impulsively rose and proposed Dodworth's health, recalling that when he himself was a bare-legged, wild-eyed, dreamy little lad on the Welsh mountains he read every word of Fenning Dodworth's earlier articles as they came out, and had never forgotten them (applause). Since those days he had met Dodworth many a time in the valley and got some resounding whacks (laughter). But he always felt, and more than ever he felt to-night, that Dodworth and he were destined to walk hand in hand on the heights, misty though those heights might be now, and hail together the glory of the sunrise that, sooner or later, had got to come (prolonged applause). My informant tells me that of all the eyes around the table Dodworth's alone were dry, and maintains that in returning thanks he ought not to have been pungent. I disagree. I want no signs of weakness in dear old Dodworth.

Dear old Dodworth? Well, no—and yet *yes*, too. I don't like him, perhaps; but there is no man whom I so delight to see, to watch, and to think of. I hope he will not predecease me. Of one thing I am sure: he will die game, and his last words will be ' —And After? ' and will be spoken pungently. And of another thing I am sure; the eminent men of all kinds will sign a petition about him to the Dean of Westminster. But there is a tradition of Philistinism in that Deanery. The voices of the eminent fall on deaf ears there, and only the roar of the man in the street is heard. Dodworth will, characteristically, not have the coarse success of lying in our Abbey. His monument will be found—piecemeal, indeed, but great, but glittering —in the diaries which I mentioned at the outset of this little essay in his honour.

A NOTE ON THE EINSTEIN THEORY

A NOTE ON THE EINSTEIN
THEORY

1923.

IT is said that there are, besides Dr. Einstein himself, only two men who can claim to have grasped the Theory in full. I cannot claim to be either of these. But I do know a good thing when I see it ; and here is a thing that is excellent in its kind—romantically excellent in a kind that is itself high. When I think of rays being deflected by gravity, and of parallel lines at long last converging so that there isn't perhaps, after all, any such thing as Infinity, I draw a very deep breath indeed. The attempt to conceive Infinity had always been quite arduous enough for me. But to imagine the absence of it ; to feel that perhaps we and all the stars beyond our ken are somehow cosily (though awfully) closed in by certain curves beyond which is nothing ; and to convince myself, by the way, that this exterior nothing is not (in virtue of *being* nothing) something, and therefore . . . but I lose the thread.

Enough that I never lose the thrill. It excites, it charms me to think of elderly great mathematicians of this and that nation packing their portmanteaus whenever there is to be a solar eclipse, and travelling over land and sea to the Lick Observatory, or to some hardly accessible mountain-top in Kamskatka, and there testing, to the best of their power, the soundness or unsoundness of the tremendous Theory. So far, the weather has not been very favourable to these undertakings. Nature, who is proud and secretive, has opposed many clouds to the batteries of telescopes. But she has had only a partial success, it seems. Some observations have been more or less clearly made, some conclusions more or less clearly drawn. And these more or less clearly point to the likelihood that what Dr. Einstein in his humdrum home evolved from his inner consciousness is all delightfully correct.

But is the British public delighted? It gives no sign of being so. Its newspapers did at the first news of Einstein's existence try, very honourably, to excite it about Einstein and even about his work. It would *not* be excited. Strange! The tamest batting of Hertfordshire *v.* Australia, the feeblest goal-keeping of Wormwood Scrubbs *v.* Hornsey Rise, the lightest word that falls from the lips of the least accomplished negro boxer, are better ' copy ' than any challenge to our notion of the Cosmos. This is all the stranger because the public is not careless of other things than Sport. Its passionate interest in archæology, for instance, rose to boiling-point, only the other day: it could *not* hear too much about the tomb of Tutan-khamen, nor tire of debating whether or not the bones of that king might rightly be disturbed. Why never a word as to the disturbance of our belief that parallel lines can nowhere converge? I haven't grudged Tutankhamen the renewal and immense enlargement of the fame he once had. I have but deplored the huge cold shoulder turned on the living Einstein.

Newton, no greater an innovator than he, is popular enough. Everybody knows something about Gravitation —and all about the apple. Perhaps if Newton had not mentioned that apple, he too would be generally ignored. It is a great advantage for a discoverer to have been inspired by some homely little incident. Newton and the apple, Copernicus and the whipping-top, James Watt and the kettle. But Einstein and——? Poor Einstein !

Men of his magnitude are not avid of popularity? True ; but this does not mean that popularity would be disagreeable to them. When the newspapers were trying to make Relativity a household word, I read an account of Einstein, written by one who knew him, and enhanced by a photograph of him. A very human person, I gathered ; far from stand-off-ish ; a player of the fiddle ; the constant smoker of a large pipe ; a genial, though thoughtful, critic of current things. I liked his views on education. Why all this forcing of a child's memory? Memory—a matter of little moment. Let the child be taught to see, and to think, for itself. And let every child be taught a trade. And ' after all,' said Einstein, dismissing tuition, ' the best thing in the world is a happy face.' It was clear from the photograph that his own face was a happy one. But I discerned in it a certain wistfulness, too—the wistfulness of a thorough good fellow whose work somehow repels the attention of that good fellow, the average man. My heart went out to him. I wished I could help him. And now, I think, I can. Hark !

Yesterday afternoon I was walking on the coast-road from Rapallo to Zoagli when I saw approaching in the distance a man of strenuous gait, and of aspect neither Italian nor English. His brow was bare to the breeze ; and as he drew near I perceived the brow to be a fine one ; and as he drew nearer still I perceived the face to be a very happy one—with just a hint in it of wistfulness, which, however, vanished at my words, ' Dr. Einstein, I presume?' He clapped a cordial hand on my shoulder ; he treated me as an old friend, as a brother, and insisted that we should sit together on the low wall that divides the road from the cliff. Presently—after he had praised the sun and the sea, and had expressed an ardent sympathy with Fascismo, and with Socialismo, no less—I said to him, ' Master (if one who is not a disciple may so address you), tell me : What was it that first put you on the track of the tremendous Theory ? ' He knitted his fine brow, saying that his memory was not a very good one ; but after a while he remembered, and spoke to me as follows :

' One winter's evening, after a hard day's work, I was sitting by my fireside—for I have an open fire in the English fashion, not a stove : I like to sit watching the happy faces in the coals—when my eye lighted on the tongs in the fender. Of course it had often lighted on them before ; but this time it carried to my brain a message which my brain could not understand. " Here," I mused, " are two perfectly parallel lines. And yet, and yet, they meet at the extreme ends. How is that ? " My friend Professor Schultz had promised to drop in and smoke a pipe with me that evening, and when he came I drew his attention to the phenomenon. He knelt down by the fender, pushed his spectacles up on to his forehead, gazed closely, and muttered, " Gott im Himmel—ja ! " I asked him—for he is a very ready man—if he had any explanation to offer. He rose from his knees and sat down on a chair heavily, burying his head in his hands. Suddenly he sprang to his feet. " Einstein," he said, " I believe I have it ! I believe that the iron-worker who made those bars must have heated them red-hot and then bent the ends towards each other." Dear old Schultz ! Always so ready !—so shallow ! I suppose I ought not to have laughed ; but I did ; and Schultz went out in some anger. It was dawn when I rose from the fireside. The fire had long ago burnt itself out, and I was stiff with cold. But my mind was all a-glow with the basic principles of Relativismus.'

' The world,' I said quietly, ' shall hear of this, Dr. Einstein.'

A STRANGER IN VENICE

A STRANGER IN VENICE

1906.

It may have been the sun that woke me; but I think it was the silence. In London the motor-omnibuses rattle and hoot vainly: my ears are inured to that din. In the country the birds 'call' me, punctually enough. But there are no singing birds in sea-girt Venice, and no traffic to detonate for the Londoner his accustomed lullaby; nor, indeed, is there any noise whatsoever, except the lapping of water against walls; and to hear that susurrus you need to be awake and intently listening. Thus, little by little, a queer emptiness intrudes itself into your slumbers, and anon you open your eyes to see what is the matter. All's well.

In the country the birds, in an ordinary city the traffic, would importune you to be up and competing with your fellows, to lose no time, to survive among the fittest. But the silence that in Venice wakes you does not rouse you. Whatever the hour of the morning, there seems no more reason for you to rise than there would be in the dead of night. Here is the dead of day. The sunlight is yellow moonlight. And you, but that you are wide awake, are Endymion. . . .

I lay as still as he, idly wondering how the Venetians had once contrived to found an empire. For surely empire-building involves early rising? And here was I, who had arrived overnight, so bereft of impulse that I was loth to

lean out and press the electric button at my bedside. I
felt sure that if I did press it there would be no answer :
I could not imagine a trill at the other end of the wire.
And if there *were* a trill, what a panic it would raise
throughout Venice !

After a while, the consciousness of hunger braced me
to press the button. Hearing no distant trill, and no
screams of terror, I assumed that I had been right in
supposing the button merely ornamental. Entered, however, a chambermaid, briskly addressing me in French.
How strange her words sounded here, in the echoing
expanse of this cinquecento room, with its arched ceiling
and its mosaic paving—this gaunt great room which
Venetian sunlight tried fiercely but vainly to make hot !
And how strange, anon, coffee and rolls tasted here—my
palate demanding for my ears the rattle of wheels on
French cobblestones, and the oaths and whip-crackings of
French cabmen !

Silence, unbroken silence ; and, in my bath, oh ! surely
Lethean water. . . .

When at length I found myself in the hall of the hotel,
there was a great surprise ready for me. I had not known
that one could walk about in Venice. I thought one had
always to step into a gondola and ' glide.' My intention
of taking a gondola to S. Mark's seemed to amuse the
keeper of the hotel. He led me to a door through which,
with a sense of lost illusion, I passed out on to dry land.
It was but three minutes' walk, he said ; and his directions
as to the route were clearness itself. Not so the route.
In Venice, that plexus of mystic alleys, I believe the very
oldest inhabitant has often to ask his way, or make guesses.
I, mistrusting my command of the language, made guesses.

Their belated outcome was that I found myself, quite suddenly, face to face with the door from which I had issued. It was not less suddenly, a few minutes later, that I was confronted by S. Mark's. But this time I said nothing. Indeed, I should not envy the soul of one who at first sight of such strange loveliness found anything to say.

Magnificent is what Ruskin wrote about it—magnificent in rhythm and colour, and having in itself much of the very quality that is in this work of Byzantine artificers. But even it, with all the great glow of it, does not describe its theme. Read it before you have seen S. Mark's : you do but admire the language. Read it after : its inadequacy frets you. Ruskin himself must have fretted—none more poignantly than that very humble great man. But one thing at least—one thing very near to the heart of a man writing about what he loves—Ruskin had achieved. He had proved his love. How can I, who am no poet, prove mine ? I must ask you to take it on trust. I loved S. Mark's. Hamlet said precisely the same thing about Ophelia ; and there has never ceased to be a hot academic debate as to whether he was speaking the truth. In a sceptic world, evidence of love is demanded. . . . Well, then, for me the church had hardly the effect of a building ; of a garden, rather ; an Eastern garden that had been by some Christian miracle petrified just when the flowers were fading, so that its beauty should last forever to the glory of Christ, and of S. Mark. But Mohammed had walked there, and his spirit haunts it yet, ranging from dome to dome, from cornice to cornice, unafraid of the Saint's own lion which, haloed, mounts golden guard in the midst, against a starred blue background ; and one almost wonders that among those stars no crescent is gleaming. Not all the multitudinous hierarchy of saints and angels that the Christians have set around the arches and in the niches could ever expel the spirit of Allah. So with a good grace they suffer his pervasion, are at amity with him, claiming him, as he, too, claims them, in a pretty glow of playful affection. East and West converge here and commingle : a dual dominion, a doubled grandeur, a doubled glory for hearts and eyes. Here is nothing of a cathedral's harshness, nothing of the lusciousness of a mosque. The tawdry is gone with the gaunt. But all that is noble and simple has triumphed in these soarings of white and grey ; and joyousness runs riot among the curves and the colours. No, I ought not to have said that. Looking at S. Mark's, one is not conscious of any frontiers there. The colours are fainting in the sunlight, and the shafts leap blithely upward, while the curves droop as if in awe. And this, again, is untrue. No contrast is anywhere visible on the façade of S. Mark's. Two spirits are there, but they are one·

Yes, a writer can give you something of the impression that a building makes on him. But the thing he would like to fix in words is not this impression, but the very aspect of the building as it is. Were I a painter . . . ah, even so, my labour would be in vain, I fancy. Many painters, from Mr. Walter Sickert backwards to John Bellini, have honourably tried to catch, on wood or on canvas, the magic of S. Mark's. In the Accademia of Venice one sees that picture in which Bellini made S. Mark's the background to a procession celebrating a miracle of the Holy Cross. It is strange and touching to see these bygone youths and maidens, in their fantastic clothes, with the church behind them, just as it is now ; and one thinks of

the generations of human creatures that have in the mean-
time shifted and fleeted across the piazza, and of the
generations unborn on which those images, from their
arches and niches, will still be gazing. . . . ' Just as it is
now ' ? Surely, S. Mark's has a sombre grandeur that we
miss in Bellini's picture of it. There was more gliding
then, and Time had but just begun to soften with his
master-hand the colours of the stones. But even then
S. Mark's cannot have been merely gay, as we see it here.
Nobly solemn it must have been from the outset. And
gay, too, delicately gay, it will be to the end of time. And
it is this very fusion that no painter whose work is known
to me has ever compassed. Mr. Walter Sickert shows to
us, darkly, the graveness and grandeur, as in a dream—the
sort of dream that may have often visited the slumbers of
Sir Christopher Wren. Mr. Sickert might almost be
suspected of having brought London air with him ; and,
as being a modern of moderns, he is less immediately con-
cerned with the object in front of him than with the air
between him and it. Yet no diffusion of London air in
the Piazza could really rob S. Mark's of its gaiety ; still
less can a mere Venetian twilight. And no brilliancy of
Venetian sun at noon, such as was chosen by Bellini, can
rob S. Mark's of its mysterious solemnity.

Some day, perhaps, some painter will achieve here his
double task. Even so, the lovers of the façade will not be
satisfied. A painter, just as he must choose one kind of
light, must pitch his easel on one special spot. But we,
the irresponsible, do not stand still : we shift from point
to point ; and at our every step the façade changes : it is
alive. The sun shifts, too, causing yet other lively
variations. How should a presentment from any one

angle, in any one light, satisfy *us*? I totter on the brink
of ' A Plea for the Cinematograph.' Recoiling, I remind
myself that painters have sometimes made almost satis-
factory portraits of human beings. Just as a man has his
especially characteristic posture and expression, by which
the painter, having found them and reproduced them, is
enabled to give us something like an equivalent for the
man himself, so has a building its especially characteristic
angle. Bellini, Mr. Sickert, and the rest have all pitched
their easels exactly facing the church. But the direct
frontal aspect is not, for us, the characteristic one ; for the
Piazza is delightfully not rectangular. Almost certainly,
our first sight of S. Mark's will have been from the south
end of the arcade of Napoleon's palace. There we are far
from facing it. We move to the middle of the arcade, and
thence to the utmost corner of it, and still S. Mark's is
oblique. We have to advance many paces along the arcade
of the Procuratie Vecchie before we are really confronted.
Doubtless it is then that the plenitude of beauty is revealed
to us. But the first vision, surely, will always be dearest
to us. We shall think always of S. Mark's as first we saw
it athwart that distance of grey pavement, turning a little
away from us, as with a certain shyness of us strangers, a
certain pride or coyness ; coyness in gaiety, pride in
grandeur.

It may be partly because there are no other horses in
Venice that so brave a show is made for us by those four
horses of green bronze which paw the air over the church's
central porch. From afar they are but a note on the façade.
But as you draw near, picking your way among the portly
grey pigeons, these horses detach themselves, stand forth,

and claim all your gaze. Two on either side of the arch, each inclining his head a little towards his fellow (with something of the perfunctorily conversational air of stage courtiers making an entrance or an exit), they paw the air delicately, haughtily, with a thoroughbred consciousness of their strength and beauty. They make one feel very small, very common; and even the sun has an anxious, servile look as he burnishes such gilding as remains on their breasts and flanks. You can see they do not consort with the little images around them. They keep themselves *to* themselves, as the phrase is. They have no allegiance to S. Mark, and are as magnificently pagan as they were on the day when they left the Grecian workshop where they had been fashioned, to be raised upon the summit of an arch of imperial Rome.

Nero wrote an ode to them. But odes perish, and empires perish; and duly the glorious team entered Constantinople, at the call of Theodosius, and there abode through eight centuries. Enrico Dandolo claimed and took them, first fruits of his victory, for Venice. It is the fate of such beauty as theirs to be ' moved on '—on to the perihelion. Little wonder such creatures as they grown vain, heartless. The sun waxed over the Venetian Republic, and waned; and these horses awaited in the twilight the conqueror, the claimant. He came. They saw him. Exquisitely, insolently, they pawed the air, pretending not to see him—the little squat man who, with his hands behind him and his feet planted far apart, stared up at them and, with the air of a millionaire ordering a meal in a noted foreign restaurant, said, ' Je les prends.' Up went the scaffolding, and down they came, and over the Alps they went rejoicing, to be the glory of Versailles.

But soon their little squat patron disappeared, went under. 'Piccadilly,' whispered the horses one to another, and waited. Up went the scaffolding, and down they came and were packed, and took the road, rejoicing. 'How rough,' they neighed in their swathings, 'the English Channel is! It is just like the Alps.' Picture their disgust when, their bandages removed, they found themselves back again in the Piazza San Marco.

Around the architrave beneath them runs a golden inscription telling, in Latin, how they, who had been 'captured by the Venetians,' were once taken away from Venice by 'the greed of an enemy'—an inscription which must surely have been drafted for the Venetians by some true-born British statesman. But no tribute can atone to them for our having let them go back to Venice—wretched little Venice, vassal of Austria, now unit of united Italy! They sulk. What right has such a hole-and-corner to be irradiated by them? Of course, after all, it is only a temporary set-back. And, as being of bronze that endures, they do not measure decades as do we, we little parcels of flesh and blood. They sulk, but they know that their fate will reassert itself. They have caught the eye of this and that American magnate. For a time they are held captive by the law that forbids exportation of works of art. But modern Italy is very commercial, and, so soon as it is in a position to dispense with the money brought in by tourists, will gladly dispose of its masterpieces to the highest bidder. Two or three generations of American magnates may have passed before that time comes. Not more than two or three minutes, according to bronze measurements. And so they are already restive, these pawing horses, these passengers; restive for the Atlantic and for the cornice of the Capitol at Washington. Yes, it is there that they will air themselves—for a while. And afterwards, where? In the midst of some yellow race, maybe. All empires perish. But perhaps our planet will last long enough for some of the dead ones to rise again. Who knows but that in the fullness of time these horses will again be overlooking Rome, their birthplace?

After I had paid my homage to these horses, I would go aside to that little estrade of marble, whose steps are guarded by two lions. For them I had a real fondness. They are not large nor beautiful. Nobody seems to know the date of them. Nobody, indeed, seems to care. Except by small boys, who sometimes ride on their backs and kick them, they are coldly ignored. Napoleon, I wager, hardly paused to glance at them. And what a sigh of relief they must have heaved when he passed them by! For they are very Venetian, these two; Venetian to the core. That is why I used always to visit them after the horses. I felt that they had hearts. They remembered Venice as she was in the zenith of her power, and had watched her decline and fall, but never had faltered in love of her. Generations of small Venetian boys have kicked them heartily, so that their sleek coat of tawny marble has been much worn away, and exists only in patches; the rest of them is a gritty white. At a distance they might be mistaken for Staffordshire ware. Yet they never murmur. Most of the other lions in Venice stand high and safe, venerable, on some eminence, and have haloes behind their manes, and spreading wings on their shoulders, and hold between their paws a scroll inscribed with the words of the blessing that Christ gave to Mark, their master. Some of them, even, have Doges kneeling to them in homage, supplicating

through them their Master's favour. None of them has
ever been kicked by a small boy. Yet is there no trace of
bitterness in the eyes of these two dilapidated lions of the
estrade. By the way, they have only three eyes between
them ; the left eye of one has been chipped out. Perhaps
they will both be blinded altogether, in time. But I know
that even so they will stick faithfully to their post, because
they were set there ; still crouching on their haunches,
mounting guard blindly, unquestioningly, even when all
around them shall be in ruins. And I think S. Mark will
call them, at last, to a high place among his lions in heaven.

They had a live lion in Venice, once. That was in the
great days of conquest. They dedicated him to S. Mark,
and gave him a gilded cage in the Piazza. He licked off
the gilding, and died. It was thought that S. Mark, had
he been pleased by the lion, would not have let him be
killed even by kindness. The Senate passed a decree that
in future no live lion should be brought into the city. The
cage was taken and sunk in the Adriatic, and is there still,
I suppose. . . . The bed of the Adriatic ! I wonder that
no sentimental archæologist has sent down divers to search
for the rings that were dropped from aboard the Bucentaur
in signum veri perpetuique dominii. Napoleon dismantled
that ornate Bucentaur when he came to dismantle Venice
of such poor pretence as she still made to dominion ; and
the old craft rotted, and is no more. But here and there
in the shifting sands of the waters about Lido must be the
rings that the Doges dropped there. . . .

Never after that decree of the Senate was a live lion
seen in Venice. But on a certain Michaelmas morning in
the fifteenth century, and in the Campo San Zaccaria, was

seen a live imitation lion ; and thenceforth, and always on that day and in that place, such lions abounded ; and one of them, at least, was there on that day in the year of grace 1906.

Nowhere in Venice is a more Venetian thing than this little, melancholy shabby Campo ; this work of so many periods ; this garment woven by so many cunning weavers, and worn threadbare, and patched and patched again, and at length discarded. Few people, and they poorest among the poor, live here now. One can hardly imagine that the well-head was ever open, ever gossiped around. Shutters interpolated in delicate Gothic windows are mouldering on their hinges ; shutters that seem hardly incongruous now that they have been blistered by so many summers, and are so faded and so crazy. Piteous is the expression of gaunt misery on the façade of the church. The old low building that straggles away from beneath the tower and is railed off from the pavement, was once a nunnery, the richest of all the nunneries in Venice. A sentinel stands at its door ; and now and again a soldier passes in or out, looking depressed. No children play here. A cat or two may be seen lying about when the sun shines. And the brightlier shines the sun the sadder seems the Campo San Zaccaria, seeming, indeed, to shrink away from the sun's rays, like a woman who has been beautiful, or like a woman who is ill.

Yet I think the place would not have thrown such a spell on me in its time of grandeur. Time was when always the greatest servants of the Venetian Republic were laid to rest here. Always on Easter Day the Doge came, in remembrance of a favour done to Venice by the nuns of San Zaccaria. Capped and canopied he came, mightily, with a great retinue ; and all the windows were frames for great ladies, and thronged was all the space of the Campo, to see him pass into church between the expectant priests. Pietro Tradonico was murdered on his way here— murdered near the little archway by which one passes out to the Riva Schiavoni. But his successors, undaunted, still came. It was here, too, that most of the great marriages were solemnised. And it was here, on the aforesaid Michaelmas morning, that a devil, in the guise of a very beautiful youth, came and, smiling, plucked by the sleeve the bride of Sebastiano Morosini, and whispered in such sweet wise that she let go the arm of her bridegroom and gave her hand to the stranger. Sebastiano would have drawn his sword, but, under a spell that the devil had cast, it stayed in its scabbard. By a frantic inspiration of the moment, he went down on his hands and knees, and, crawling, roared, insomuch that the devil (having, like all the devils of that day, a share of simplicity) mistook him for the lion of S. Mark, and instantly vanished. Nor, so far as we know, did he ever reappear. But Sebastiano's stratagem, S. Mark's miracle, had laid such hold on the hearts of the Venetians that every man who was soon to be married would come on Michaelmas morning to the Campo San Zaccaria, and crawl once around the well-head, roaring. Thereby, it was thought, he assured for himself happiness of wedlock : his wife would never be inconstant to him, even in thought. She, the intended wife, accompanied him, with her parents, and with his parents, to see the pious little ceremony performed. All through Michaelmas morning the Campo San Zaccaria was crowded. Carpaccio painted a picture of the scene : a scene after his own heart ; a picture that one can well imagine : the demure, angelic, very small bride, with her downcast eyes ; and the rapt, angelic bridegroom, with eyes upturned and lips parted, down on his delicate hands and pied knees, by the well-head ; and the whole pretty throng of serried figures around these two. One can imagine the picture, but not, alas ! see it. It was stolen from the church of San Zaccaria, and, like the devil who tempted Sebastiano's bride, has never been seen again.

It is a far cry from this century to the fifteenth. But Venice, in the long interval, has stood still. Time and her enemies have been active. It is they who have changed her. She has submitted. But one would say that what has not been taken from her she has quietly kept. In her prime, she sucked the blood of the East, and the draught was sedative. Something of the essential immutability of the East is hers beneath all the changes that Time and her enemies have wrought on her. It seemed to me not so very strange, on Michaelmas morning, to see mimicked in all simple earnestness the action of Sebastiano Morosini.

My Venetian friends had laughed, told me there was no chance of seeing any such thing. But I, with an obstinacy foreign to my nature, rose very early on Michaelmas morning, and went to my beloved Campo. If any bridegroom came, he would not care to have tourist's eye on him. So I posted myself well within the shadow of the arch where the Doge was murdered. . . . A fool's errand it seemed to be, after I had waited half an hour or so ; and I (determined to say nothing of the matter to my Venetian friends) was on the point of going away, when through the other gateway, came a small party of peasants, all in their Sunday best. There were six of them—two middle-aged men, two middle-aged women, and a young man, and a girl. For a minute or so they stood talking. Then the young man detached himself from the group, tossing his sombrero to an elder, and came across to the well-head. There, having crossed himself, he went down on his hands and knees, and did as Sebastiano had done before him ; and, little though the roaring may have been like a lion's, I did not once smile on my way home along the Riva Schiavoni.

Always as I passed along that Riva, I would try to imagine Venice as she was in her plenitude of wealth and power. Here, just here, I would remind myself, were launched those great argosies which imposed the will of the Venetian Republic on the cowering peoples far and near. I tried to picture the quay thronged with the stern unbending citizens of a State whose policy was nothing if not practical. But the scene would never compose itself. It was easy to dot the Riva with figures gay and delicate, from Carpaccio's canvases, from Bellini's, and I could see argosies launched in quest of the blue bird, carrying charts drawn up by dreamers. But Venice hard-headed, Venice imperious and imperial, always baffled my fancy. Nowhere in her weakness is a sign that she was once strong, as other cities have been strong—nowhere the remnant of a rampart to hint that she was not always at the world's mercy. But everywhere in her melancholy are signs of the gaiety that was hers. Lightness, enchantment, gaiety : this is what we can see with conviction as we peer into the past. And it was for this, I told myself, that she arose from the waters and blossomed into loveliness. Power came to her. An accident ! Power fell away from her. What matter ? The rose had but lost its thorns.

To me there was nothing piteous in that period of Venice's history which we call ' the decadence '—that period of which Ruskin could not trust himself to speak, so great was his sorrow, his horror. To him ' the decadence ' was not inevitable : had Venice not given way to ' the sin of pride ', had she remained simple and pious, she need not have lost her power. Ruskin felt that had he been alive he might have saved her. And his wrath against her was as vivid as though he had been preaching in S. Mark's five centuries or so before the publication of ' The Stones of Venice.' It was the moral fervour in Ruskin that gave such intensity to his noble style. By reason of it he is, just as a writer, worth a hundred or so of merely philosophic gentlemen like you and me. It narrowed him, as a thinker, and put him again and again in the wrong. But how gloriously wrong and narrow was he ! And, when he was right, how divinely ! I wish we were a little like him. To us, the merely philosophic, Venice's ' decadence ' was a thing that could not have been avoided. A great city or nation is like a human being : sooner or later it must decline ; no elixir can save it. And on the ' decadence ' we can look back quite calmly, appreciating what in it was graceful and delightful.

And to me, as I have suggested, the fall of Venice was not in her loss of power, but in her loss of gaiety. She seemed to have been most truly accomplishing her destiny in the days when she gave herself over to be ' the masque of Italy.' The eighteenth century was for me her perihelion. And it was the period that most readily evolved itself. The figures from Carpaccio, from Bellini, would come at call. But the figures from Guardi and Longhi were there uninvited. Cloaked and hooded and masked, there they were, leaning one to another, whispering, softly laughing, in every gondola that passed me in the night. Aye ! and in the day, not less. The gondola, even under noonday sun, seems always an offshoot of the night, and diffuses the night's own glamour, and is indissociable from those dark and mystic revellers who, on the sun-steeped pavement of the Piazzetta, turned day into night, just as they turned night into day throughout the alleys round about the Ridotto.

Not the Piazza, grand and gay, but this Piazzetta, this Placelet, in its untroubled gaiety, was for me the area most redolent of that which in the past of Venice was most real to me. Here it was that the ghosts of the eighteenth century jostled one another most closely, and were most at home. Here had been for them, when they lived, the properest venue of their frivolity. The two columns that stand there, with their vast capitals and with the tiny S. Theodore lost aloft with his crocodile on one of them, and with the big lion striding away from him on the other, have all the appearance of a joke—a joke that is still irresistible. And the Ducal Palace, with its vast sheer surface of diapered brick superimposed on those two frail white colonnades —is it not as daintily unreal as it is wonderful ? I tried to realise that it was here that awful conclaves were held, and awful edicts issued. Here, at this gate, a herald proclaimed to the populace that Marino Faliero had. . . . No !— never could I see the place save as background for masquerade. And at night, with the electric light cast up on its expanse, I saw it always as cardboard, or as a backcloth of stretched canvas.

' Theatrical ' ! I have heard dull people apply that term to the whole of Venice. I doubt not they would apply it, with an equal sense of having said the correct thing, to the whole of fairy-land. Unreal, certainly, Venice seems. But her unreality is as of a dream, not as of any *décor* that could be devised by a showman. Often I felt afraid that I was actually dreaming. You know what it is to awake excited by the consciousness that a profound idea has just passed through your mind. You recapture it, and lo! it's nonsense. Often in Venice I feared just such another disillusion. Impalpable Venice! Frail vision! Was I not presently to awake and find that I had been dreaming of—Brighton? the whole delicate network of alleys, all these campi and campanili, would they not anon vanish, with the very archipelago from which they had been conjured, into the water or the air?

I *had* often been assured that Venice was 'quite spoilt now.' And I daresay that for any one revisiting her after the lapse of many years there might be shocks. There are steamboats on the Grand Canal. There are cinematograph shows in the Ridotto. There are more factory chimneys than of yore, when you look back from the lagoon. Oh, yes ; the old friends of Venice find plenty to growl at. And I, twenty years or so hence, shall be growling with the best of them, no doubt, and wondering at the innocent rhapsodies of some newcomer. But he is likelier to be right than I. To one who has known and loved a place in past years, even improvements are offensive. Not that more steamboats and more factory chimneys would be an improvement. I regret, on principle, those which are already there. But I deny that they really matter. Such is Venice's beauty that things ugly in themselves do not stand out the uglier by contrast : they are absorbed into the glamour. When night falls on Chelsea 'the factory chimneys become campanili.' But in Venice, because sunlight cannot dispel her mystery, the factory chimneys are always campanili. And the steamboats are always gondolas. No one need cavil at their aspect. They have taken to themselves just that night-like quality which the gondola has. Of course, I regret the noise they make. It is the only noise that has ever been made in Venice, city of silence. But electricity will soon hush that down. Then, perhaps, I shall complain that I miss the romantic, old-world sound of the steam issuing from the funnels.

Meanwhile, it is easy to escape that sound. Not along the Grand Canal, glorious though it is, do you find essential Venice. The beauty that is hidden away, not the beauty revealed, is the city's essence. The panorama of the Grand Canal enraptures you, and the rapture passes. There is no more to be said, no more to be seen, and you drift away, from that obvious loveliness, into the side-canals or into the alleys. *They* do not pall. They are so many and, for all their variety, so subtly akin that you never can definitely remember the features of any one of them. They are always new to you, always mysteries, 'bazaars of smiling chances,' leading to you know not what fresh and sudden revelation.

Pausing on this or that little bridge of battered marble, and gazing down and along, one can take in a canal's aspect more perfectly than one can from a gondola. . . . These mouldering old palaces, gazing so ruefully down at their reflections, wondering whether they really look like *that*, not knowing that they are more beautiful, so, than they ever were ; these wan reaches of ghost-enclosing palaces, with the plaster peeling off them and showing their bricks in patches, and with the clear green water lapping and sapping their foundations. See how time has thinned with rust the iron bars of the windows, and with dust has thickened the cobwebs! Soon it will be hard to know which are the bars, which the cobwebs. . . . I think it must have been there, in *this* palace, that lived that strange couple, the Misses Bordereau. Perhaps the younger Miss Bordereau is still living, still there. No, there can only be ghosts behind those shutters. See, on the walls yonder, that faint blur of colours—yellow and purple. Can it ever have been a fresco? It can never have been lovelier. And yonder, see how blithely, among all this decay, the vine renews its youth! But who will pluck the grapes? Ghosts do not eat grapes.

Musing in some such wise, I would turn away from the parapet, and from the contemplation of sunlit death, and pass over into the shadows where life was. They are ravines, these alleys. The blue strip far overhead might be an awning, so very faint is the light down here. Coming straight from the sunshine, one can hardly see, and is apt to collide with the inhabitants. ' *Piano, Signore,*' said an aged pedlar with whom I had clumsily collided. ' Who are you a-shoving of? ' is of course what he ought to have said, and would have said had he received the advantage of an English education. But they are a quiet, soft-speaking lot, these poor Venetians. Even when they quarrel—a thing which they seem to do often, and with great intensity—it is a greater lesson in good manners than a breach of good manners to stand and watch them. Neither of the two parties to the quarrel raises his voice ; and neither interrupts the other : each takes his turn at reviling and listening. With the utmost velocity and variety of gesture and facial contortion, one man emits a torrent of words whose evident ferocity is in quaintest contrast with the quietness of his utterance. The other man, with a perfectly impassive face, waits till the torrent has spent itself, and then, presto ! is torrential on his own account, and receives as patient a hearing as any orator could desire. There is not the fraction of a pause between his peroration and his antagonist's exordium ; but never do the two things overlap. When the women quarrel, it is in precisely the same excellent manner, but with less animation. A man and a woman quarrelling is a sight not vouchsafed to the tourist. Indeed, I seldom saw a man talking to a woman. Potent still are the oriental habits that came with the infusion of oriental blood. Women and men are severely segregated. One almost wonders that the women are allowed to appear at all. A woman never appears alone. Always she has, or is, a chaperon. I had rather expected to behold some specimens of the Venetian young woman as she used to appear annually on the walls of Burlington House—a Titian-haired young person of opulent outlines, attired in vivid rags, smiling boldly as she lolls against a wall, with a half-eaten pomegranate in her hand. The actual Venetian young woman—a very small, plain, homely person in black, with a black shawl strained around her shoulders—would be much puzzled by the Royal Academy's version of her ; and her chaperon, I am sure, would be much annoyed. But for their fine eyes, and the powder on their cheeks, these women might easily be mistaken for English pew-openers. And neither the eyes nor the powder on the cheeks can lessen the effect of intense respectability. There is never a sparkle in the eyes, and one guesses the powder on the cheeks to be a traditional substitute for the yashmak.

Subjection, oriental subjection, is the note of these women.
The men are orientally predominant. They carry themselves with a certain grave pride, in impressive contrast
with the grave meekness of the women.

I do not say that these Venetians seem less happy than
the people one sees in the streets of London. Indeed,
despite the fact that they are not, as their ancestors were,
rulers of the sea, disporting themselves in the centre of a
tremendous and soul-stirring empire, they seem to contrive
somehow to look happier than we, who are so much in the
movement. Often, passing through the streets of London,
I have wondered what on earth the inhabitants would look
like if they had no longer the thought of their pre-eminence
to sustain them. Perhaps individual happiness is rather a
matter of climate than of collective renown. The Venetians
are despised by the rest of Italy as a feckless people. They
have no industries. Some glass is made in Murano, some
lace is made in Burano, but in Venice itself nothing is
made, and no one seems to know what the factory-chimneys
are there for. The Venetians get a little out of the foreigners,
and, for the rest, take in one another's washing, and trust
to S. Mark. 'Parasiti' they are called by the rest of
Italy. Yet they seem to respect themselves ; and, in their
way, in these quiet, dark, very clean alleys, seem to be
rather an enviable than a despicable race. I took always
great pleasure in passing among them, and then out again
into a sudden burst of sunshine, and some new enchantment, and across another bridge, into the shadows of other
alleys, or into the yet deeper, cooler shadows of San this
or Santa that.

Venice plays havoc with one's sense of time, and I know
not at all how many days of enchanted dawdling I had

spent when I found myself wondering, one night, on the terrace of my hotel, whether it were possible that I should soon have had enough of it. That one should rise hungry from a meal is a rule which many doctors prescribe, and many cooks enforce. Sufficiency, we are to suppose, is the little sister of excess. I reflected that on the spiritual plane, certainly, this theory was a sound one. It would be impious to stay in Venice till I felt that I had had enough. I must go with the enchantment full on me. I owed Venice that.

Examining my soul, I found no symptoms of disenchantment. And yet . . . was Venice *quite* so marvellous to me as she had been? In his 'Venetian Life' Mr. Howells declared that he never, in the whole three years of his sojourn, passed through the Piazza San Marco without feeling as poignantly as at first the wonder of it. But I— already was not I beginning to be habituated there? Had I been *quite* so surprised, so exalted, this morning, as when first the vision was vouchsafed to me? Of course not. The alleys, the back-canals—yes, *they* were as fresh to me as ever. But the time might come when they too. . . . I rose uneasily, threw my cigarette into the water, and leaned against the parapet. Silently out of the darkness came a gondola, heading for the steps. There was luggage in the prow, English luggage; and raptly gazing at the terrace there was a party of English people. . . . It was how many days ago that I had arrived, just at this hour? —Days? It seemed years. And I knew that I must have gazed out of the gondola, with just that rapt look, wondering if Venice could be so lovely by day as she was by night, and wondering who was that romantic Venetian leaning against the parapet. For these newcomers *I* was

the romantic Venetian, a part of the magical land-seascape ;
and they to me were ordinary English tourists, coming to
Venice for the first time, with that in their eyes which had
gone from mine. . . . Yes, I would go away to-morrow
morning. I would go to Padua. And next morning I went.

When I emerged from the railway-station of Padua, I
was confronted by three very strange and terrible monsters
with gaping jaws. I let my luggage be thrown, as a sop,
to one of them, but I refused to be swallowed personally.
They were but hotel omnibuses. But I had forgotten, in
Venice, that such things existed. I had forgotten what it
felt like to drive. I would rather walk.

The way to the town was along a wide road with tram-
lines through a flat and barren landscape. The road seemed
to ' give ' alarmingly at every step, so accustomed was I
now to treading on marble.

What was that tall, square, brown building yonder ?
A factory, I supposed. But why that large hole through
it, from the ground upwards ? And why did the building
stand in the middle of the road ? Because, as I presently
realised, it was a gateway. Whenever in the future I
should look out from the window of a railway carriage
on my way from London to the country, I should be able
to imagine that the factories clustered near the line were
Romanesque gateways, not hives of human drudgery.

I passed quickly on. What was this ? Another gateway ? No, this *must* be a factory. No, it was a church.
How oppressive it was, this vast, square surface of unfaced
bricks, this sad thing that had stood for centuries unfinished,
this amorphous, dead bulk ! I passed quickly on. Coming
to a bridge, I paused, from force of habit, to gaze down

from the parapet. Could this be water?—this viscid, sluggish stuff, of a blue so unwholesome that it must have been got by some aniline dye. I thought of the clear, chrysoprase waters that I had left. I passed quickly on —' for the great desire I had to see fair Padua.'

'Fair'! I must look neither to the right nor to the left. It was wrong to judge a city by its outskirts. Imagine a stranger judging Oxford by its outskirts! In the old days, scholar-pilgrims came from Padua to Oxford, from Oxford to Padua. I, too, would ' haply institute a course of learning and ingenious studies.' Yes, I had lived too softly in Venice. I had let my sensibility sway me too much there. In Padua I would austerely improve my mind. I would forget Venice.

But here a physical difficulty beset me. You know how, after a voyage, you feel—sometimes for days—the motion of the boat. Well, gently though a gondola rocks, it is as haunting as any steamer or sailing vessel. At every step —here along this high-road—I felt within me the motion of the gondola. It quavered insistently, like the Venusberg motive in the ' Pilgrims' March.' I would march it down. Petrarch had loved Padua. So had Tasso. Cavour, in a well-cut frock-coat of white marble, and trouserings to match, beamed a secular benediction on me. He looked thoroughly at home here, in the piazza named after him. I had seen him somewhere in Venice. A furtive and negligible intruder he had seemed there, despite his pedestal. But here he had the air of a host. ' *Siete il benvenuto*,' he seemed to purr, rubbing his plump marble hands together. I fled into my hotel. I plied myself with food and with wine.

I asked my way to the university, and was directed to

the Via Otto Febbraio. A strange setting for an old jewel —this street of big blatant shops with plate-glass windows ! (In Venice all the shops had been so tiny, so modest.) My eye was caught by a break in these shops, and by what I took to be a small music-hall. It looked new and prosperous. I might go there this evening. . . . It was the university.

I turned down a side-street, under an arcade. All the side-streets seemed to be arcaded ; and yes, they were picturesque ; but how heavy, how coarse, in comparison with—no ; it was not fair to make that comparison. I quoted to myself the last two lines of ' Venezia,' an emotional sonnet which I had once read in an American magazine :

> Let other cities with each other vie ;
> Venezia is *sui generis*.

But you remember the little boy who was taken for a while to live with the fairies, and how hard and how vainly, when he came home again, he tried to forget them. I, too, had lived with the fairies.

I tried to kill time. But time is a hydra. For every quarter-of-an-hour that you kill, up crop several others. Would the sun never set ? Would dinner-time *never* come ?

I dined, at length, in a garish restaurant, with horrible *art-nouveau* figures of the months frescoed on the ceiling (twelve months in Padua !), and I bitterly thought of the morrow. The waiter advised me to visit the Teatro Garibaldi. There was a new piece by Signor Borsetti. I was in a mood to clutch at straws.

The curtain had not yet risen. But there was a preliminary

entertainment that seemed to please the Paduans very much indeed. A swallow had flown into the auditorium, and was skimming wildly around, too terrified to alight anywhere. Round and round the stuffy and gaudy little theatre flew the fowl of the air, and the audience made noises at it. Looking from it to them, and from them to it, I wondered whether, after all, man is the finest of God's creatures. The band struck up, and for a moment the bird dipped, quivered, seemed as though it would fall. Then it flew faster and faster. I could see an open window in the topmost gallery. Why could not the bird see it, too, and escape from this inferno? Poor senseless creature!

What the play was about I know not. The bird never rested, ever revolving in the glare of the chandelier. And yonder, all the time, was the open window, and the pure freedom of the night. The whole thing seemed vaguely like a parable. A parable of what? . . . And I—I !— had presumed to pity the bird's lack of sense.

The manager of the hotel was sorry I had to leave so soon ; oh yes, there was a train for Venice : I should just have time to pack ; he would have my bill made out at once.

It was a very slow train. My heart outran it a thousand times on the way. No lover was ever more impatient than I. No one had ever been more in love than I was. To think there were people who did not know Venice—people who had never yet lived ! And those who did know her —did they know her as I did? No, she had told the secrets of her heart to me alone. She was waiting for me. I was on the way.

With the selfishness of a lover, I had forgotten all about the bird—the captive to whom I owed my freedom.

I laughed aloud to myself, remembering my solemn academic theory about the dangers of sufficiency. I laughed to think that I had solemnly acted on this theory—prig and fool that I had been ! Well, I had come to my senses. I could afford to laugh now. But why *wouldn't* the train go faster ?

At last we were crossing the lagoon. And presently I was quit of the railway station, and out on the canal. There were scarves of clouds across the moon, and Venice looked more than ever visionary in that faint twilight. I felt not as though I had come to her in her sleep, but as though she, a vision, had come to me in mine ; as though she, not I, were the ' revenant.' Was I truly awake ? Yes, it was Venice that was sleeping. And ' *Piano, gondoliere,*' I said. ' *Lentamente . . . Piano . . .* '

THE SPIRIT OF CARICATURE

THE SPIRIT OF CARICATURE

1901.

LAST night, very vividly, I dreamed a most preposterous dream.

On the pillowed verge of sleep, I had been propounding to myself an old vexatious question : Why is true caricature so rare and so unpopular in England ? The delicious art of exaggerating, without fear or favour, the peculiarities of this or that human body, for the mere sake of exaggeration —why can it not be naturalised among us ? A certain Italian artist did, indeed, in the late 'sixties, come and try to force it on us. Awhile, from him, we had true caricatures. We did not take kindly to them. We thought them offensive and ' not like.' The pressure of our English atmosphere gradually overbore that temerarious alien. Before the close of the 'seventies he had begun to draw caricatures of a mild and gentlemanly kind, suitable to the susceptibilities of a mild and gentlemanly nation. He was succeeded by one who frankly eschews the art of caricature, to the gratification of every one, and does always a charming portrait, with a playful touch adventured here and there if his sitter be not very eminent, nor very ugly, nor of noble birth. There are others—men of wit, accomplished draughtsmen—who design symbolical cartoons or make rough sketches with the purpose of ridiculing the members of one or other of the two great political parties. In them caricature comes of a moral impulse. It is not the sheer desire and irresponsible lust for bedevilling this or that human body; and it is, accordingly, not successful as caricature; nay! it is not caricature at all. The public believes it to be caricature, and forgives the perpetrators of it because they are evidently strenuous partisans— *quia multum amaverunt.* Are there any other pretenders to the art? Can one point to any one who dares. . . . Can one find. . . . But the poppies were nodding to my eyelids. I was asleep. . . .

I knew not how, by whose prayers, the national conversion had been made. But there was no doubt of the fact that there had arisen a sudden and widespread demand for true caricature. Meetings had been held in all the principal cities. Even the rural districts were clamorous. The Government, bowing beneath the storm, had caused to be hewn, and to be imposed upon the vacant pedestal in Trafalgar Square, a statue of Carlo Pellegrini, in atonement for England's evil influence on him. Moreover, in the waste places of South Kensington had been builded a vast 'School of National Caricature'. The edifice was complete now. It was a dream (within a dream) of electric lamps, hot-water-pipes, skylights, cocoanut-matting, and all else that is supposed to evoke and foster artistic sensibilities in the young. Royalty had opened it. Archiepiscopacy had blessed it. Hundreds of the young had enrolled as students. Still something was lacking. There was no professor. The country was being scoured, scoured stringently for a suitable person. They had not yet found any one possessed of the true spirit of caricature, any one carrying forward the tradition imported and dropped by Pellegrini. I began to feel uncomfortable. I knew that I, as a last resource, should be 'approached,' with a view to my acceptance of the post. And here, sure enough, was the grey-bearded deputation approaching me. With the horrible impotence of the dream-stricken, I was unable to run away. Vainly I strove to warn them off. Vainly I was arguing with them. I was pointing out to them that Pellegrini was a great executant, that my own technique was so vague as to disqualify me for the honour thrust upon me. They replied that only the *spirit* of the caricaturist was essential, and that only in my work did it burn. Blushing, I demonstrated that the creative artist was the last person who should be employed as teacher. Able to do the trick himself, he had no pathetic desire to see it done by others. ' That's how it's done ! '—the smiling conjuror's formula—was all he could vouchsafe. He had no enthusiasm for teaching. The sterile lovers of an art, they were the proper teachers of it. They wanted to see the trick done, and would see that it was done. ' Besides,' I added, ' they alone know *how* it can be done. The creative artist works by instinct : he knows not how, by what mystic secret of soul and hand, his work evolves itself. He does not care to know. He has no theories. He can formulate no rules. The conjuror could, if he would, lay bare his processes ; but the artist, never. The only people who can show how to do things are the people who cannot do them.' ' No doubt,' said the spokesman ; ' but it is our national custom to appoint as teachers the artists who have done things. It inspires confidence. False confidence, no doubt ; but still confidence.' ' Then,' I cried, ' our system of art schools is a sham ; and I, for one, will not fatten on it.' ' It is a wholesome sham,' was the answer. ' The aim of our art-schools is not (we admit this in confidence) to produce artists. Artists can be produced only by themselves. Art-training is simply a means of keeping young persons out of mischief. As such, it is necessary to the common-weal. This new craze for the art of caricature is a chance which we could not afford to miss. We are determined to make the best use of it. But we are helpless without a Professor. Young persons must not be fobbed off with a mere dummy. They *must* have an ornament to look up to. Come ! We appeal to your civic sense. South Kensington is waiting for you. So is England. The future of the race may depend on your answer. Be a man ! ' In sheer weariness I consented. The deputation smiled itself out. I was to deliver the inaugural address to the students at nine o'clock next morning. What was I to say ? Was there anything to be said ? I looked through a portfolio of my own drawings, wondering how they had been done, or what rules could be deduced from them. (It was a painful dream.) Somehow at length, under stress of necessity, with infinite trouble, I hewed out a few first principles, a few hints. . . . The scene dissolved, dissolved into cocoanut-matting and hot-water-pipes. I was about to address the students. Their wide-open eyes and mouths made me horribly nervous. I cleared my throat, loudly, so loudly that I awoke.

My first sensation was one of intense relief. But this presently gave way to resentment that all my labour in the preparation of the address had been so much labour lost. I could recollect more or less exactly the notes I had made. Hating waste, why should I not expand them for a magazine ? Here, then, is the gist of what I would have said to those phantom students. I do not suppose it will be illuminative. What I said to that phantom deputation about the futility of tuition by a creative person is really quite true. However, their reply (that the public loved such tuition) was equally true. So I need ask no one's pardon.

As people do sometimes make passionate demands for a thing without knowing at all what it is, I was not going to assume that my pupils knew the nature of true caricature. I was going to start with my definition : the art of exaggerating, without fear or favour, the peculiarities of this or that human body, for the mere sake of exaggeration. I was, then, going to deal with the two reasons for the unpopularity of such portraits—(a) the impression that they imply in their maker irreverence and cruelty, (b) the impression that they bear little or no resemblance to their originals. The second impression can hardly be cured. It is the result of inherent lack of imagination. Caricature, as I shall demonstrate anon, demands acute imagination from its beholders. The first impression may be gently argued away. A well-known art critic once chid me in print because I ' never hesitated to make a good man ridiculous.' Why should I ? Caricature implies no moral judgment on its subject. It eschews any kind of symbolism, tells no story, deals with no matter but the personal appearance of its subject. Therefore, the caricaturist, though he may feel the deepest reverence for the man whom he is drawing, will not make him one jot less ridiculous than he has made another man whom he despises. To make the latter ridiculous gives him no moral pleasure : why should it give him any moral pain to make ridiculous the former ? He imports into his vision of the former nothing which is not there : why should he subtract anything from his vision of the latter ? He portrays each surface exactly as it appears to his distorted gaze. 'For the mere sake of exaggeration,' I said. But he does not, even, make conscious aim at exaggeration. He does not say, ' I will go for this " point " or that.' If he did, he would be no caricaturist. He exaggerates instinctively, unconsciously. 'But,' you might urge, ' when he finds that the result is pain to his subject's friends and joy to his subject's enemies, he ought to desist from his art.' Maybe, if either the pain or the joy were reasonable, were justified. But they are not. Both are foolish. All that can be expected of the artist is that he should demonstrate their folly from time to time. Even that is rather much to expect of a man passionately absorbed in his own work.

The friends of a man are pained by a caricature of him because they think it will make him despicable to other people ; his enemies rejoice for the same reason. They could not harbour a sillier fallacy. Such laughter as may be caused by a caricature is merely æsthetic. It corresponds with such tears as are shed at sight of a very beautiful statue. I do not pity Venus when I see her statue in its chamber at the Louvre ; yet there are tears in my eyes. I do not despise Disraeli when I look at Pellegrini's picture of him ; yet I laugh. It is even so with any one else who is affected by beauty and by absurdity. If caricature affected us at all towards its subject, it would affect us favourably towards it. Tragedy, said Aristotle, purges us of superfluous awe, by evocation, and comedy likewise purges us of superfluous contempt. Even so might idealism of a subject purge us of superfluous awe for it, and caricature purge us of superfluous contempt. If the sight of Pheidias' masterpiece ministered to our reverence for Venus, she would pass out of our minds as we passed from the gallery.

If the sight of Pellegrini's Disraeli satisfied our hostility towards Disraeli himself, we should forgive him all. Indeed, does nothing of the kind happen? This theory of purgation has a dangerous charm for me. I have often been tempted to attribute the Romans' decline in faith to the fair statues of gods and goddesses imported from Greece by victorious generals. The extraordinary preponderance of ugly men among those who have shaped the world's history—may it not be due to the chance they gave to the contemporary caricaturists? No no; let me be sensible. Caricature never has had moral influence of any kind.

The 'chances' given by ugliness! Do not misunderstand this phrase. Do not mistake me to mean that there is any such thing as a 'good subject' or a 'bad subject' for caricature. There are obvious subjects and devious subjects. A short man is a more obvious subject than a tall man, for shortness is held to be in itself ridiculous, and thus the uninspired caricaturist will prefer to draw short men. Most caricaturists, being uninspired, have followed this line of less resistance; and thus has arisen the foolish convention of a head invariably bigger than its body. By the man in the street caricature would probably be defined as the art of putting a big head upon a little body. Indeed, so strong is the convention that it affected even Pellegrini, Daumier, and other masters. To you, thoughtful reader, I need hardly point out that in a caricature of a tall man the head ought to be not magnified but diminished. The big-head convention would be all very well if caricature were no more than μίμησις τῶν φαυλοτέρων. But the true art of caricature is much more than that. The master of it never discriminates his subjects, has no preferences. He cares no more whether his subject be tall or short, grotesque or comely, than whether he be a ' good ' man or a wicked. He is able to strike as ridiculous effects from the exaggeration of a handsome face and fine figure as from the exaggeration of a street-boy's butt. Hermes or Caliban—it is all one to him. Superficially, indeed, you might guess that Hermes would give him less trouble than Caliban. Sir Willoughby Patterne was said by his creator to be ' so correctly handsome that a slight unfriendly touch precipitated him into caricature.' Truly, the more sublime the subject the more easily may it be burlesqued. But there is a vast difference between burlesque and caricature. Mr. Meredith has confused the two things. Burlesque consists in application of incongruity. Caricature consists merely in exaggeration. The one works from without its subject, the other from within. To burlesque a statue of Hermes, you need but put a top hat on its head. To caricature it, you must exaggerate its every limb and feature. To caricature Sir Willoughby Patterne would have needed the hand of a master. The process of striking a ridiculous effect would have been far more difficult in his case than in the case of an already absurd-looking man. That is what I mean when I speak of ' obvious and devious subjects.' When I object to the notion of ' good and bad subjects,' I mean that handsomeness *can* be made as ridiculous as ugliness. You ask me, ' How about a subject who is neither handsome nor ugly ? ' In that case, merely, it is the lack of features that must be exaggerated. Through intensification of its nullity, such a subject may be made as ridiculous as any other.

Perfect burlesque may be achieved with a touch. The

perfect caricature (be it of a handsome man or a hideous or an insipid) must be an exaggeration of the whole creature, from top to toe. Whatsoever is salient must be magnified, whatsoever is subordinate must be proportionately diminished. The whole man must be melted down, as in a crucible, and then, as from the solution, be fashioned anew. He must emerge with not one particle of himself lost, yet with not a particle of himself as it was before. And not only must every line and curve of him have been tampered with : the fashion of his clothes must have been re-cut to fit them perfectly. His complexion, too, and the colour of his hair must have been changed, scientifically, for the worse. And he will stand there wholly transformed, the joy of his creator, the joy of those who are privy to the art of caricature. By the uninitiated he will not be recognised. Caricature, being so drastic in its methods, demands in its beholders a keen faculty of imagination, as I have said.

The perfect caricature is not a mere snapshot. It is the outcome of study ; it is the epitome of its subject's surface, the presentment (once and for all) of his most characteristic pose, gesture, expression. Therefore I should not advise any young caricaturist (however quickly perceptive) to rely on one sight of his subject. On the other hand, let him not make too long a delay, inasmuch as too great familiarity blunts impressions. There is another golden rule, which, if he be worth anything at all, he will know without being told it : he must never draw ' from the model.' While he looks at the model, he is bound by the realities of it. He sees everything as it is. He cannot suborn his pencil to magnify or diminish the proportions, to add or abate one jot. In fact, he cannot begin to caricature. It is only in recollection of his subject that the unconscious process of exaggeration begins to work. Let him allow this process to run its course, leisurely, to his finger-tips. Then, not till then, may he clutch his pencil.

The perfect caricature is bold in its execution, simple and ingenuous to its beholder as a wild flower. Of course, in every work of art elimination and simplification are essential. In a caricature they are doubly so. For a caricature is a form of wit, and nothing so ruthlessly chokes laughter as the suspicion of labour. And, even as brevity is the soul of wit, so is a small scale not less necessary than an air of spontaneity to the perfect caricature. Nor can that spirit abide on a large surface. If you have seen either Pellegrini's big painted caricature of Mr. Whistler, or Mr. Whistler's of a certain art-patron, you will not require me to labour this point. Big canvases and oil paints are fit only for 'seriously serious' art. For a serious art which makes frivolity its aim, a sheet of plain foolscap, a pen or pencil, and a little water-colour are the proper media.

The perfect caricature is in itself a beautiful thing. For caricature, not less than for every other art, beauty is a primal condition. The beauty of a work of art lies not at all in the artist's vision of his subject, but in his presentment of the vision. If the ladies on the chocolate-boxes were exactly incarnate, their beauty would conquer the world. If Daumier's senators and deputies were exactly incarnate, life would be intolerable. Yet no discreet patron of art collects chocolate-boxes ; and that series by Daumier is one of the loveliest and most precious things in the whole world.

The most perfect caricature is that which, on a small

surface, with the simplest means, most accurately exaggerates, to the highest point, the peculiarities of a human being, at his most characteristic moment, in the most beautiful manner.

Looking back at what I have written, I do really think that my inaugural address to those phantom students might have been illuminative. I am almost sorry that I have materialised it in this essay. So much knack of exposition and ratiocination as it betrays inclines me to doubt whether my creative power in caricature can be quite so strong as I had supposed. However. . . .

AUBREY BEARDSLEY

AUBREY BEARDSLEY

1898.

To all who knew him, and to all who did not know him but are lovers of lineal art, Aubrey Beardsley's death has been the occasion for much sorrow, an irreparable loss. But there is, I think, some consolation in the thought that he did not die suddenly. Though he died, a great artist, in his first youth, and at the very opening of life, as life is usually reckoned, Fate did not deal with him unfairly, did not take him, as she has taken others, with a kind of brutal treachery, before the fulfilment of all the work that was in him. From his quite early boyhood, Aubrey Beardsley had known quite well that his life would inevitably be a short one, and it was to this knowledge, partly, that we owe the great range of his achievement in art. Fate had given him a prematurity of power that was in accurate ratio to the appointed brevity of his life, and, in the exercise and the development of his genius, Aubrey Beardsley never rested. He worked on always, with a kind of desperate courage, and with a degree of force and enthusiasm that is given only to the doomed man. He knew that he had no time to lose. At the age when normal genius is still groping for its method, he was the unerring master of his method. He died, having achieved master-pieces, at an age when normal genius has as yet done little of which it will not be heartily ashamed hereafter. Normal genius is in no hurry. If it be struck down suddenly before its prime, it leaves no great legacy to us : we can only rail against Fate.

But Aubrey Beardsley was bound to die young. All his friends knew that as well as he did. The only wonder was that the fine thread of his life was not severed sooner. I remember that when I first saw him I thought I had never seen so utterly frail a creature—he looked more like a ghost than a living man. He was then, I believe, already in an advanced stage of pulmonary consumption. When I came to know him better, I realised that it was only by sheer force of nerves that he contrived to sustain himself. He was always, whenever one saw him, in the highest spirits, full of fun and of fresh theories about life and art. But one could not help feeling that as soon as he were alone he would sink down, fatigued and listless, with all the spirit gone out of him. One felt that his gaiety resulted from a kind of pride and was only assumed, as who should say, in company. Perhaps one underrated his strength. When he was alone, he must have worked at his drawings almost without intermission. It is a curious thing that none of his visitors ever found him at work, or saw any of his rough sketches, or even so much as his pen, ink, and paper. It was his pose to appear as a man of leisure, living among books. Certainly, he seemed to have read, and to have made his reading into culture, more than any man I have ever met ; though how he, whose executive industry was so great, managed to read so much, is a question which I have never quite solved : I can only suppose that he read very rapidly. The literature of the Restoration and of the Eighteenth Century had always especially appealed to him. He delighted (oddly enough) in Voltaire. He was supposed to have read the whole of the *Comédie Humaine*, and he had all the modern schools of France at his finger-tips. He was a good Latin scholar, too, though ill-health had curtailed his schooldays, and he had practically had to teach himself all that he knew. His conversation had always the charm of scholarship. Though not less modest than are most young men, he had strong opinions on most subjects, and he expressed himself with clear precision, and with wit. But he had not the physical strength which is necessary to the really great or inspiring talker. With him, there was always the painful sense of effort. I remember an afternoon I spent with him, at his house in Cambridge Street, soon after *The Yellow Book* was started. He was in great form, and showed even more than his usual wit and animation, as he paced up and down the room, talking, with all his odd, abrupt gestures, about one thing and another, about everything under the sun. I am a very good listener, and I enjoyed myself very much. Next day I heard that his mother and his sister and a doctor had been sitting up with him till daybreak. He had been seized, soon after I had left, with a terribly violent attack of hæmorrhage, and it had been thought, more than once, that he could not live through the night. I remember, also, very clearly, a supper at which Beardsley was present. After the supper we sat up rather late. He was the life and soul of the party, till, quite suddenly, almost in the middle of a sentence, he fell fast asleep in his chair. He had overstrained his vitality, and it had all left him. I can see him now, as he sat there with his head sunk on his breast : the thin face, white as the gardenia in his coat, and the prominent, harshly-cut features ; the hair, that always covered his whole forehead in a fringe and was of so curious a colour—a kind of tortoiseshell ; the narrow, angular figure, and the long hands that were so full of power.

Last month, when Beardsley's death was announced in the newspapers, the general public must have read the news with some surprise. The 'Beardsley Boom,' as it was called, had begun with *The Yellow Book*, and it had ceased with *The Savoy*, and Beardsley had, to all intents and purposes, been forgotten by the general public. For more than a year, he had been living in this or that quiet place to which invalids are sent. There were no new 'Beardsley posters' on the London hoardings. The paragraphists of the London Press gradually let him be. His book of fifty collected drawings created no outcry, for even the book-reviewers could no longer assert that he did not know how to draw, and the tattlers at tea-parties had said all they had to say about him long ago, and had found other subjects for their discussion. But, while it lasted, how fierce the 'Beardsley Boom' had been! The public, as I need hardly say, never admired Beardsley's drawings. It thought them hideous. If the 'Beardsley woman' could have been incarnated, she would have been singularly unattractive. Then how could anyone admire her on paper? Besides, she was all out of drawing. Look at her arm! Beardsley didn't know how to draw. The public itself could draw better than that. Nevertheless, the public took great interest in all Beardsley's work, as it does in the work of any new artist who either edifies or shocks it. That Beardsley's really did shock the public, there can be no doubt. There can be equally little doubt that the public like being shocked, and sympathy would, therefore, be superfluous. But, at the same time, there are, of course, people who do honestly dislike and deplore the

morbid spirit that seemed to inspire Beardsley's work, and
at such people I should not wish to sneer—on the contrary,
I respect their feeling, which I know to be perfectly
genuine. Nor would I seek to deny that in Beardsley's
work—more especially in some of his early work—there is
much that is morbid. But it must be remembered that,
when he first began to publish his drawings, he had hardly
emerged from that school-boy age when the mind is
generally apt to brood on unpleasant subjects, and much
of his work, which some people regarded as the sign of a
corrupt nature, was really the outcome of a perfectly
normal phase of mind, finding an abnormal outlet through
premature skill in art. I think, too, that he had a boyish
delight in shocking people, and that it was often in mere
mischief that he chose, as in many of his grotesques for
the *Bon-Mots* series, to present such horribly ugly notions.
Many of those who knew Beardsley only through his general
work imagined that he must be a man of somewhat for-
bidding character. His powerful, morbid fancy really
repelled them, and to them the very beauty of its expression
may have seemed a kind of added poison. But I, or anyone
else who ever saw him at his home, knew that whatever
was morbid in his work reflected only one side of his
nature. I knew him to be of a kindly, generous, and
affectionate disposition ; a devoted son and brother ; a
very loyal friend.

He lived, when I first saw him and till some two years
later, in Cambridge Street, where he shared a house with
his mother and sister. Here, every Thursday afternoon,
was held a kind of little *salon*, which was always well
attended. Aubrey himself was always present, very neatly
dressed, handing round cake and bread-and-butter, and

talking to each of his mother's guests in turn. There were always three or four new drawings of his passed from hand to hand, and he was always delighted with praise from any of his friends. I think it was at these little half-formal, half-intimate receptions that one saw him at his best. With all his affectations, he had that inborn kindliness which is the basis of all good manners. He was essentially a good host.

I have mentioned his grotesques for the volumes of *Bon-Mots*. These, if I am not mistaken, were among his very earliest published drawings, and simultaneously with them he was working at that great task, the illustration of the *Morte d'Arthur*, on which he spent such a wealth of skilful and appropriate fancy. In the drawings for the *Morte d'Arthur* he was still working, of course, under the influence of Sir Edward Burne-Jones—an influence which was oddly balanced by that of Japanese art in the drawings which he did, at this period, for his own pleasure, and of which *La Femme Incomprise* is a good example. The well-known drawings which, later, he made for *The Yellow Book* were, with their black masses, and very fine lines, arrived at through simplification of the method in *La Femme Incomprise*. These were the drawings that first excited the wrath of the general public and of the book-reviewers. Most of the qualified art-critics, also, were very angry. They did not know what to make of these drawings, which were referable to no established school or known method in art. Beardsley was not at all discouraged by the contempt with which his technique was treated. On the contrary, he revelled in his unfavourable press-cuttings, knowing how little they signified. I think it was in the third number of *The Yellow Book* that two pictures by hitherto-unknown artists were reproduced. One was a large head of Mantegna, by Philip Broughton; the other, a pastel-study of a Frenchwoman, by Albert Foschter. Both the drawings had rather a success with the reviewers, one of whom advised Beardsley 'to study and profit by the sound and scholarly draughtsmanship of which Mr. Philip Broughton furnishes another example in his familiar manner.' Beardsley, who had made both the drawings and invented both the signatures, was greatly amused and delighted.

Meanwhile, Beardsley's acknowledged drawings produced a large crop of imitators, both here and in America. Imitators are the plague to which every original artist is exposed. They inflict the wounds which, in other days, the critics were able to inflict. With the enormous increase of the Press and the wide employment of ignorant and stupid writers, bad criticism has become so general that criticism itself has lost its sting, and the time when an artist could be 'snuffed out by an article' is altogether bygone. Nowadays, it is only through his imitators that an artist can be made to suffer. He sees his power vulgarised and distorted by a hundred apes. Beardsley's *Yellow Book* manner was bound to allure incompetent draughtsmen. It *looked* so simple and so easy—a few blots and random curves, and there you were. Needless to say, the results were appalling. But Beardsley was always, in many ways, developing and modifying his method, and so was always ahead of his apish retinue. His imitators never got so far as to attempt his later manner, the manner of his *Rape of the Lock*, for to do that would have required more patience and more knowledge of sheer drawing than they could possibly afford. Such a design as the 'Coiffing' which came in a late number of *The Savoy*, and which has often seemed to me the most exquisite thing Beardsley ever did, offered them no possible short-cut to talent. To trace the sequence of technical phases through which Beardsley passed, would be outside the scope of this brief essay. But I should like to remind my readers that, as he grew older, he became gradually more ' human,' less curious of horrible things. Of this tendency the best example is perhaps his ' Ave atque Vale,' in *The Savoy*. Nothing could be more dramatic, more moving and simple, than the figure of that Roman who mourns his friend. The drawing was meant to illustrate one of Catullus' Odes, which Beardsley himself had thus rendered :

> By ways remote and distant waters sped,
> Brother, to thy sad grave-side am I come,
> That I may give the last gifts to the dead,
> And vainly parley with thine ashes dumb :
> Since she who now bestows and now denies
> Hath ta'en thee, hapless brother, from mine eyes.
>
> But lo ! these gifts, the heirlooms of past years,
> Are made sad things to grace thy coffin-shell,
> Take them, all drenchéd with a brother's tears,
> And, brother, for all time, hail and farewell !

These lines, which seem to me no less beautiful than the drawing itself, were written shortly before Beardsley left England for the last time. On the eve of his departure, he was received by Father Sebastian into the Catholic Church, to which he had long inclined. His conversion was no mere passing whim, as some people supposed it to be ; it was made from true emotional and intellectual impulse. From that time to his death he was a pious and devout Catholic, whose religion consoled him for all the bodily sufferings he underwent. Almost to the very last he was full of fresh schemes for work. When, at length, he knew that his life could but outlast a few more days, he awaited death with perfect resignation. He died last month, at Mentone, in the presence of his mother and his sister.

Thus ended this brief, tragic, brilliant life. It had been filled with a larger measure of sweet and bitter experience than is given to most men who die in their old age. Aubrey Beardsley was famous in his youth, and to be famous in one's youth has been called the most gracious gift that the gods can bestow. And, unless I am mistaken, he enjoyed his fame, and was proud of it, though, as a great artist who had a sense of humour, he was perhaps, a little ashamed of it too, now and then. For the rest, was he happy in his life? I do not know. In a fashion, I think he was. He knew that his life must be short, and so he lived and loved every hour of it with a kind of jealous intensity. He had that absolute power of 'living in the moment' which is given only to the doomed man—that kind of self-conscious happiness, the delight in still clinging to the thing whose worth you have only realised through the knowledge that it will soon be taken from you. For him, as for the schoolboy whose holidays are near their close, every hour—every minute, even—had its value. His drawing, his compositions in prose and in verse, his reading—these things were not enough to satisfy his strenuous demands on life. He was himself an accomplished musician, he was a great frequenter of concerts, and seldom, when he was in London, did he miss a 'Wagner night' at Covent Garden. He loved dining out, and, in fact, gaiety of any kind. His restlessness was, I suppose, one of the symptoms of his malady. He was always most content where there was the greatest noise and bustle, the largest number of people, and the most brilliant light. The 'domino room' at the Café Royal had always a great fascination for him : he liked the mirrors and the florid gilding, the little parties of foreigners and the smoke and the clatter of the dominoes being shuffled on the marble tables. Yet, though he took such a keen delight in all the manifestations of life, he himself, despite his energy and his high spirits, his frankness and thoughtfulness, seemed always rather remote, rather detached from ordinary conditions, a kind of independent spectator. He enjoyed life, but he was never wholly of it.

This kind of aloofness has been noted in all great artists. Their power isolates them. It is because they stand at a little distance that they can see so much. No man ever *saw* more than Beardsley. He was infinitely sensitive to the aspect of all things around him. And that, I think, was the basis of his genius. All the greatest fantastic art postulates the power to see things, unerringly, as they are.

A SOCIAL SUCCESS

Persons of the Play

TOMMY DIXON	*(Aged 30, clean-shaven, debonair)*
THE DUCHESS OF HUNTINGTON	*(Handsome, a widow, aged 40)*
THE EARL OF AMERSHAM	*(Full-bodied, sleek, red-faced man of 53. Fair hair turning grey, small fair moustache)*
THE COUNTESS OF AMERSHAM	*(Pretty, romantic-looking woman of 29. Dark hair)*
HENRY ROBBINS	*(Three or four years older than Tommy. Rather stiff and formal. Long, serious face, clean-shaven)*
HAWKINS	*(Valet acting as butler)*

A SOCIAL SUCCESS

SCENE : Drawing-room of Tommy Dixon's flat in Mount Street.

TIME : Pre-War. Between 11 and 12 p.m.

> [*The room is of a conventionally luxurious kind. Facing you is a wide bay-window with drawn curtains. Between the window and the door there is a three-fold screen of Spanish leather. In front of the window is a writing-table, with a telephone. Book-shelves in plenty. Bright fire in grate. Along the mantel-piece and all around the mirror, a serried array of invitation-cards, big and little. Two arm-chairs near fire. Also a low table with the inevitable Tantalus and syphons, a bottle or two of mineral water, cigarettes, etc.*
>
> *At a large round table (in the middle of* your *side of the room) the game of poker is being played.* TOMMY *(facing you) has on his right side* LADY AMERSHAM, *and on his left the* DUCHESS. *Next to the*

DUCHESS *is* LORD AMERSHAM ; *next to whom, on* LADY AMERSHAM'S *right, is* HENRY ROBBINS. TOMMY *has a goodly pile of counters before him, interspersed with banknotes and gold. There is also a large ' pool ' in the middle of the table. The four other players have but a few counters apiece.*

As the curtain rises these four players are taking up the cards dealt them by TOMMY.]

TOMMY (*fingering the remainder of the pack*)
Cards, Duchess ?

DUCHESS (*sighing as she lays down her cards*)
Hopeless.

TOMMY
Amersham ?

LORD A. (*laying down his cards*)
Pass.

DUCHESS (*fingering the pool*)
And such a pool !

TOMMY
Robbins ?

ROBBINS (*shaking his head*)
I must pass.

A SOCIAL SUCCESS

TOMMY

Come ! I can't be left to rake all this in ! (*Persuasively*)
Lady Amersham !

LADY A. (*after a slight tremor*)

Two cards, Tommy.
> [*Takes the two cards, utters a little cry of
> relief.* TOMMY *looks at his own cards.*]

TOMMY

H'm, I'll stay as I am.

DUCHESS

What cards he has ! (*Looks fondly at him.*)

TOMMY

Yes, it's too bad to ask you all here, and then . . .

LADY A. (*pushing forward her counters*)

I stake my all !

TOMMY (*with a shrug of the shoulders*)

Sorry. Raise you a fiver. Can't help it.

LADY A. (*holding out her hand to her husband*)

Two fivers, Jack.
> [LORD AMERSHAM *produces banknotes from
> pocket-book, and passes them to his wife,
> not taking his eyes off* TOMMY, *whose
> hands are below the level of the table.*]

LADY A. (*Lays down one note on table and says to* TOMMY :)
There. (*She lays down the other.*) See you for a fiver.

TOMMY

Four aces.

[*He shows his cards.*]

LADY A. (*ruefully*)

Oh . . .

DUCHESS

Didn't I . . .

> [LORD AMERSHAM *meanwhile has leapt to his feet.*]

LORD A. (*leaning across the table with forefinger outstretched to* TOMMY, *and in a voice hoarse with passion*)
You scoundrel !

TOMMY

W-what ?

LADY A.

Jack !

ROBBINS

Really !

DUCHESS

The man's mad !

LORD A.

How did you come by the ace of clubs ?

TOMMY (*vaguely*)

How did I . . .

168

LORD A.

How did *I*, sir?

> [*Turns up his own cards, confronting* TOMMY
> *with ace of clubs.*]

LADY A. (*faintly*)

Don't call him ' sir ' !

ROBBINS

It must have got in out of the other pack.

LORD A. (*relentlessly*)

The other pack's pink. This one's green. This card of
mine has a green back : so has—our host's.

TOMMY (*pursing his lips, and gazing wide-eyed at* LORD
AMERSHAM'S *ace*)

H'm.

DUCHESS (*to* LORD A.)

You don't—you can't mean——

> [*She rises from table.*]

LADY A.

Mean what ?

LORD A.

I mean that I have been watching him very narrowly
for the past half-hour, and . . .

TOMMY (*springing to his feet*)

A pretty thing to do—watching a man under his own
roof, and then slandering him and . . . and . . .

LORD A.

Undo your sleeve-links ! Lay bare your arm !

TOMMY (*staggering back, stammering*)

You seem to—to forget there are ladies present.

ROBBINS (*who has also risen, to* LORD A.)

You don't mean . . .

LORD A.

I mean that I'm going to see if that was the only ace
the fellow had up his sleeve.

> [*He darts round the table (in front of the*
> DUCHESS, *who has retreated a few
> steps) and seizes* TOMMY *by the left
> arm.*]

LADY A. (*her hands clasped in agony*)

Tommy, say it isn't true !

TOMMY (*wrenches his arm out of* LORD AMERSHAM'S
grip ; then sullenly)

Wouldn't make much difference what I said. May as
well own up and (*with a broken laugh*) make a—clean wrist
of it. It's what they call ' a fair cop.' (*Produces a card
from left-hand shirt-cuff and throws it on table*) Ace of
hearts. (*Two cards from right-hand shirt-cuff*) Ace of
spades. Ace of diamonds. (*Feels in breast pocket of coat*)
Other court cards. (*Throws down these*)That's the lot.

> [*Hang-dog he stares down at table.* ROBBINS
> *and the two women have slowly retreated
> further and further away from him.*

A SOCIAL SUCCESS

LADY AMERSHAM *now buries her face in her hands.* THE DUCHESS *gazes up in petrified agony to the ceiling.* ROBBINS *stands with chin sunk on breast.*]

LORD A. (*bringing clenched right hand down on open palm of left*)

And this—this is the man we—we've broken bread with! This is the man we've all of us for the past few years been calling Tommy till, damn it, I hardly remember his surname. . . . Dixon, that's it. . . . Dixon the card-sharper.

[*A low wail escapes from* LADY AMERSHAM.]

Enid, my darling, go and get on your cloak. This (*with increasing horror*) is the man I put up for Bains's—the one remaining club that *nobody* can get into—and got him in. You'll send in your resignation to-night, sir.

[ROBBINS *utters a groan.*]

TOMMY

Don't you try to bully *me*! I'm a member of Bains's and there I'll stick—till they expel me.

LORD A.

I'll go straight there—Enid, you can drop me there—and I'll tell every man in the place. (*To* TOMMY) And there'll be an end of *you*!

[*Simultaneously* TOMMY *presses button of electric bell in wall behind him. Another groan from* ROBBINS.]

171

LORD A. (*turning on* ROBBINS)
As for you, Mr. Roberts——

ROBBINS
Robbins.

LORD A. (*to* TOMMY)
You had the impudence to-night to ask me to second your friend for the Club . . .

TOMMY
And you said that any friend of mine . . .
> [LORD AMERSHAM *makes an explosive sound.*
> HAWKINS *meanwhile has appeared in*
> *answer to the bell.*]

TOMMY
The lift, Hawkins.
> [*Exit* HAWKINS.]

LORD A.
I won't set foot in your lift. Enid, my darling, come— by the staircase. Duchess, I'm unspeakably . . .

DUCHESS (*moving with them to the door*)
I feel that the very staircase is polluted. (*Makes a gesture as to gather up her skirt, and audibly inhales between her teeth.*) I should like to be carried to my car.
> [*Exeunt the* DUCHESS *and* LORD *and* LADY
> AMERSHAM. TOMMY *stands motion-*
> *less, with bowed head and clenched*
> *hands.* ROBBINS *stands on the other*

172

side of the room, with arms folded, look-
ing him up and down. At sound of the
slammed front-door he moves slowly
towards the door of the room, still
gazing sternly at his friend, and goes out,
shutting the door after him. TOMMY
looks at the door, delightedly clasps his
hands, beams, looks around, and anon
begins to pirouette gracefully around the
room. As he reaches the table where the
glasses and decanters are, he stoops
down (facing you), and airily pours
some whisky into a tumbler, then some
Apollinaris. As he does so, the door
opens noiselessly, revealing ROBBINS *in*
hat and overcoat. ROBBINS *gives a*
violent start, strides down the stage. Just
as TOMMY *raises the tumbler to his lips*
ROBBINS *from behind grips his friend's*
wrist with one hand and firmly removes
the tumbler with the other. TOMMY,
confounded, returns his stare. ROBBINS,
not relaxing his grip, raises the tumbler
to his nostrils, sniffs it, looks quickly
round from it into his friend's eyes.]

ROBBINS

Arsenic? (*He quickly sniffs tumbler again, then with*
another piercing and probing glance at TOMMY) Strychnine?
(*Sniff and glance repeated*) Hydrochloric? . . . Anyhow
. . . (*He carefully inverts the tumbler and spills its contents*
to the carpet) that's the place for it.

TOMMY

You haven't much feeling for my carpet, old boy.

ROBBINS

A human life—even the life of a man who has sunk so low as you—is more sacred to me than any carpet.

TOMMY

Ah, you see, you don't derive an income from carpets. *I do*. This is one of Dixon's extra double-pile hand-woven, and . . .

ROBBINS

That's what makes it all the more horrible that you have (*gesture to card-table*) done *that* . . . If you had been a *poor* man. . . .

TOMMY

I can't see that that would have been any excuse.

ROBBINS

I am glad you are not lost to all sense of decency. . . . In the old days, when we had those rooms in the Temple——

TOMMY

Happy days !

ROBBINS

Ah, if you'd only stuck to the Bar ! If your father had only lived . . .

TOMMY

And left me to shift for myself—yes. It's that confounded unearned increment that has undermined me.
Good-night, old man. Rising barristers can't afford to
associate with card-sharpers.

ROBBINS (*with a groan*)

How long have you been——? (*Gesture to card-table.*)

TOMMY

Well, as a matter of fact, to-night was my début.

ROBBINS (*throws back head, and sighs deeply*)

When I think of the splendid social position you'd
made for yourself—made without effort—the great houses
you had the run of—the great people and the gay and
noble who . . . To-night, when I heard the Duchess
calling you ' Tommy ' . . . Charming woman, the Duchess
(*meditatively removes hat from head*). It was very good of
you to ask me to-night, Tommy. . . . And Lord and
Lady Amersham—what charming people ! The best type
of our old English——

TOMMY

You're becoming maudlin, old boy.

ROBBINS

Ah, Tommy, I can't take those people so lightly as you
do. Perhaps that's the reason why they never seem to
follow me up. . . . When I think of you dragging out a
miserable existence in some shady foreign watering-
place . . .

TOMMY

I shall do nothing of the sort.

ROBBINS

You mean . . . ? (*Pointing to tumbler.*)

TOMMY

You certainly are maudlin. As if a fellow can't have a simple whisky and Apollinaris without being suspected of suicide !

ROBBINS

Then I didn't save your life ? (*Points down to the stain on carpet.*) There wasn't a drop of . . . ?

TOMMY

If you doubt my word (*gesture to telephone*) ring up the Home Office and ask them to send round the Public Analyst, to analyse the carpet.

ROBBINS (*in a constrained voice, staring down at the stain*)

Oh, . . . well, . . . I'm glad.

TOMMY

Don't take it so hard, Robbins. You showed great presence of mind and good feeling, and all that. But somehow (*mixing another drink for himself*) you chaps with trained legal faculties are always so awfully wide of the mark. . . . Now mind ! (*indicating tumbler*) This is for *me*. I will not have you debauching my carpet. (*Takes a deep draught.*) As for dragging out a miserable existence in a shady foreign watering-place that you've found in the pages of Thackeray—nonsense ! I shall stay just where I am.

ROBBINS

And face the music ? Tommy, I shall stand by you.

TOMMY (*with a queer look*)

That's the worst of old friends—no shaking 'em off !

ROBBINS

Tommy !

TOMMY

I'm sorry. (*Lays hand on* ROBBINS' *shoulder*.) I don't mind old friends. Hang it, no : I don't want to be a hermit. Freedom !—that's all I wanted. And now (*flings wide his arms, gazing up beatifically*) I've got it !

ROBBINS

Freedom ? Of course there'll be no question of gaol. But to be publicly branded, as. . . . Freedom ? Freedom from what ?

TOMMY

Why, from the whole cursed dog's-life I've been leading. Freedom to sit down cosily and lead my own life. Tranquillity, independence, quiet fun. Books. Pipes. D'you know, Robbins, I haven't been able to settle down to a book since . . . heaven knows when . . . ever since I got caught up into that infernal social merry-go-round. To-night I've jumped off. Jolly neatly, too. Pleasing air of finality about the whole thing.

ROBBINS

Tommy, this bravado is more heart-rending than if you . . .

TOMMY

Bravado? When a man's just brought off a very delicate and ticklish job which he——

ROBBINS

You *didn't* bring it off. You were found out.

TOMMY

Robbins, you're hopeless. How many more times must I tell you that my object was just *to* be found out?

ROBBINS

To be found out?

TOMMY

You lawyers aren't able to understand the simplest statement unless it's made on oath in a witness-box by a man whom you can browbeat. . . . *To* be found out. . . . Mind you, I only tell you this in strictest confidence. You must swear not to——

ROBBINS

I never betray a confidence. But do you ask me to believe . . . What possible motive——

TOMMY

Haven't I told you my motive was to get right out of Society, as it is called?

178

ROBBINS

Society as it is *called*? Society is Society. And—surely there are other ways of getting out of it than . . .

TOMMY

No, there aren't.

ROBBINS

You could have gone away—settled quietly down in the country—Cornwall——

TOMMY

But I love London. Not a drop of Cornish blood in my veins. Never happy away from London. Never do get away from it properly. It's in my bones.

ROBBINS

Well, what was to prevent you from leading a quiet life here in London, if you really wanted to?

TOMMY

Ah, there speaks the man who isn't a social success!

ROBBINS

You needn't remind me of that.

TOMMY

My dear chap, I'm only congratulating you. . . . . A social success is a man who can't call his soul his own. Might as well be a trapped rabbit. Better. Agony not so prolonged. Moment he shows his face—' Can you lunch to-morrow?' If he stays at home ' Trr-trr-trr': telephone bell : ' Can you lunch to-morrow ? ' Oh, that eternal ' Can you lunch to-morrow ? ' !

ROBBINS

Very easy to say you're sorry you're engaged.

TOMMY

Oh, of course, I always said that—and horribly true it was. ' Then can you lunch the next day ? '—' Next day ? No, I'm afr——' ' Then the day after ? '—' That's Thursday, isn't it ? N-n——' ' Then Friday ? Or *any* day next week ? ' And there one is. They've no shame.

ROBBINS

But if you had said firmly—if you had given them to understand, once and for all——

TOMMY

I'm not that sort of fellow. I can't hurt people's feelings : I'm not a boor. If I were, I should never have been a social success. It was my confounded easy-going amiability and general niceness that got me into society—and prevented me from getting out.

ROBBINS

But——

TOMMY

Oh, I did what I could. All sorts of things. I went in for a diet of sea-weed biscuits. No good. All the hostesses instantly had sea-weed biscuits for me. Sea-weed biscuits became the rage. There were sea-weed luncheons, sea-weed dinners, sea-weed suppers. Last summer, at the

Foreign Office reception, I pretended to be drunk. Not a soul there but refused to see anything at all strange about me. There was a time when I used to sit in the bow-window of Bains's, wearing a motor-cap and a frock-coat. They all admired my splendid moral courage. My dear fellow, I've tried scores of ways. This (*gesture to card-table*) was the only way out. Desperate remedy? Desperate disease. And here I am—cured. (*Finishes his whisky and Apollinaris.*) By the way I'm sorry about Bains's. I should like to have got you in.

ROBBINS (*gloomily*)

Oh, I should never have got in.

TOMMY (*consolingly*)

No.

ROBBINS

Then why did you put me up?

TOMMY

Well, you were always saying you'd like me to. And —there it was: my amiability again. Unable to say ' No '.

ROBBINS (*nods his head, sinks down on to edge of arm-chair, and heaves a deep sigh*)

I had often wondered—forgive an old friend's frank-ness—what it was that people saw in you. *I've* always liked you. But why should every one else? ' Tommy '— ' Tommy ' to every one. Nobody ever called me Harry.

TOMMY

Is your name—er—Henry?

ROBBINS

There! After all these years! You didn't even know my Christian name.

TOMMY

I knew your initial was H.

ROBBINS

You never called me H.

TOMMY (*kindly*)

H.

ROBBINS

Thanks, old fellow.

TOMMY

Odd! When Amersham called me 'Dixon' to-night, I felt I must go down on my knees for sheer joy and gratitude. (*Rolls it over his tongue*) 'Dixon.'

ROBBINS (*gloomily*)

'Dixon the card-sharper.' That's how you'll go down to posterity.

TOMMY

Think so? I shall be satisfied if the name sticks to me while I live! ... It was my being 'Tommy' to the husbands, as well as to the wives that always sickened me. ... I've a sense of honour.

ROBBINS

Do I understand that you were in the habit of behaving
dishonourably?

TOMMY

Oh, no. Only, *I'm* the sort of fellow who happens to
be attractive to—I know it sounds fatuous—but attractive
to—well, to the *sillier* sort of women, don't you know?

ROBBINS

Married women?

TOMMY

Well, lots of silly women get married. There's no
competitive examination. But not necessarily *married*
women (*waves his hands vaguely*). Widows. All kinds.

ROBBINS

All widows?

TOMMY

The *sillier* sort of widows—like the Duchess.

ROBBINS (*rising from arm-chair*)

You really mean that the—there was a chance of your
becoming a—a sort of Duke?

TOMMY

I think there was a sort of danger. May have been. . . .
One never knows where one is with those people. They've
such a lot of time to waste, and there's so much make-
believe. . . . The married women, they don't want you

to make love to them. But they want you to *want* to make love to them, all the time. And if they think you're making love to anyone else—or if they think anyone else is *wanting* you to *want* to—then there's a deuce of a row. And of course a man's one idea is to avoid rows. Only, the wear and tear of avoiding a row is worse than the row itself. And of course there always *is* the row, anyway. . . . *Was,* at least. *Was !*

ROBBINS (*after a pause*)
I'd no idea how much you were sacrificing.

TOMMY
No ? (*fingering the strewn cards on the table*) I say, I'd no idea how much I was winning. The struggle for freedom is a jolly lucrative thing. (*Gathering up notes and gold*) What shall I do with it all ? Can't send it back to those people. Look like climbing down. . . . How much did you lose ?

ROBBINS (*waving away proffered banknote*)
Send it all to some charity.

TOMMY (*pocketing the notes and gold*)
Right. To-morrow morning. Society for the Relief of Decayed Card Sharpers or Something. . . . I say: here's the ace of clubs,—*and* the other one. These I must have framed and glazed. Big white margin, with suitable inscription. Gilt frame, with bird of freedom perched on it. (*Carries the two aces around as though seeking the place where they would look best on the wall*) Look at *those* cards ! (*Inclusive gesture to the invitation*

cards over the mantelpiece) Waste-paper ! . . . Look at that telephone ! Mute for evermore.

> [TELEPHONE-BELL : ' Trr-trr-trr ! ' *Both men start and stare at telephone.*]

TOMMY (*raising a finger*)

Hark to the swan-song !

> [TELEPHONE-BELL : ' Trr-trr-trr, trr-trr-trr.']

TOMMY

Pathetic, isn't it ? (*Goes across to writing-table and raises the receiver*) Halloa ! Yes. (*An instant later, with a violent start :*) Duchess ? Duchess of—*Huntington ?* . . . Yes, of course I knew your v-voice, but . . . *What ?* (*His face becomes positively blank with horror*) You're sorry you . . . What ? . . . Worse things in the world than cheating at . . . But, my dear woman . . . *What ?* . . . (*Stares wildly at Robbins*) But . . .

> [*Covers receiver with one hand, and, turning to* ROBBINS, *asks in a hissing whisper,* ' What shall I say ? ' *Puts it back to his lips.*]

Fact is I—I'm married already—years ago—unfortunate entanglement . . . N-no. No chance of a divorce. Lost sight of her. Living somewhere in the wilds of New Zealand. *Absolutely* respectable. N-no, to-morrow I can't. Lunching with Robbins—my friend, H. Robbins. . . . Come round to you in the morning ? Well, I . . . Well . . . No, not tea, I have to go out to tea . . . Y-yes, I could come in later, I suppose—d-delighted—but——

> [*At about the middle of this monologue, the*

> *electric bell of the front-door has sounded,*
> *audible through the open door of the*
> *drawing-room.* ROBBINS *has made a*
> *gesture at hearing it.* TOMMY *has done*
> *likewise. At the word ' but '* HAWKINS
> *ushers in* LADY AMERSHAM, *who flings*
> *herself past him into the room. Exit*
> HAWKINS.]

LADY A. (*to* ROBBINS)

Where—— (*Sees* TOMMY, *who stands stupefied, receiver in hand*) Tommy, my dear—dear——

> [ROBBINS, *much embarrassed, takes his hat*
> *and moves towards door.*]

TOMMY

Robbins ! Don't *go*—don't ! (*To* LADY A.) What on earth . . .

LADY A.

Tommy, I think I must have been mad. The whole thing was so sudden. Forgive me. Don't—don't look at me like that. In your hour of need I turned from you. As if there weren't heaps of things worse than cheating at cards ! Though all the world condemn you—Tommy, the old life is over : I throw in my lot with you. (*Throws her cloak from her shoulders, letting it fall to the ground*) For ever.

> [ROBBINS *awkwardly picks up cloak and*
> *stands holding it on his arm.*]

TOMMY

For—for ev——

186

A SOCIAL SUCCESS

LADY A. (*with quick suspicion*)
Who are you telephoning to?

TOMMY (*mechanically dropping receiver on to its
groove*)
Enid, for heaven's sake—think of Amersham. . . .

LADY A.
I think of the man whom Amersham has exposed,
ruined, hounded down—the man I——

TOMMY
But, Enid, he was quite right——

LADY A.
According to his own lights, yes. Oh, I don't judge
him. Who am I that I should cast the first stone at him
—I, who deserted you just when—— (*Buries her face in
her hands for an instant. Unburies her face*) 'Think of
Amersham'? I think of him as last I saw him, bounding
up the steps of Bains's—and I telling the chauffeur to
drive me home. It wasn't till I was almost at my door
that I realised my baseness.

TOMMY
But,—but—Robbins, do help me! Tell her she seems
to be forgetting all about *my* baseness.

ROBBINS (*awkwardly*)
I certainly do think——

LADY A.
You! Who are you that you should come betwee——

187

ROBBINS

That's just what had struck me, Lady Amersham.

TOMMY (*under his breath*)

Snob !

LADY A. (*to* TOMMY)

As for your baseness, I glory in it. But for it, my true nature would never have been tested. I thought I was shallow, and a coward, and selfish. I find myself a woman of—of——

TOMMY

Heroic mould. Oh, you're all that, Enid. And that's just why you positively mustn't have anything to do with a pariah like me. . . . Come ! (*Makes movement towards door*)

LADY A. (*very firmly*)

It is when a man becomes a pariah that he finds out who are his true friends.

> [TELEPHONE-BELL : ' Trr-trr-trr.' TOMMY
> casts agitated glances at it, snatches up
> receiver, and babbles.]

TOMMY

Yes—yes—I was so sorry—called away—will you hold the line ?—I——

LADY A. (*darting towards him*)

Tommy, I insist on knowing who——

> [*At this moment is heard a loud knocking at
> the front-door.*]

TOMMY (*to* ROBBINS *while he himself stands guard over telephone*)

Tell Hawkins—quick—not at home—to anybody.

> [ROBBINS *crosses to door, opens it, starts back, almost closing door.* LORD AMERSHAM'S *voice is heard saying,* 'Mr. Dixon still up? Very well. I'll go straight in.']

TOMMY (*to* ROBBINS)

Stop him!

ROBBINS (*throwing* LADY AMERSHAM'S *cloak behind a chair*)

Hadn't Lady Amersham better——? (*Points to screen as he darts out into hall. His voice and* LORD AMERSHAM'S *are heard without.* LADY AMERSHAM *has darted towards screen.*)

TOMMY

Don't do that! Only done on stage! Most compromising thing possible.

LADY A. (*with a look of quick illumination*)

Exactly! So much the better!

> [*She darts behind the screen and, as the door flies open, it is too late to stop her.*]

LORD A. (*to* ROBBINS)

I tell you——

> [*He sees* TOMMY, *who has backed to a corner, and strides towards him.*]

Tommy (*with faint jauntiness*)

Ah—er——

Lord A.

Tommy, your hand!

[Tommy *half puts out a wavering hand.*]

Lord A.

Come! Don't bear malice, Tommy. (*Grips the hand and shakes it vehemently.*) There! Not another word!

Tommy (*gazing from screen to card-table*)

But——

Lord A.

Forget what I said! I'm an impetuous, blundering fellow. But you must admit—— Hang it, Tommy! I had some provocation. What you did—it—well, it wasn't playing the game, *was* it?

Tommy

No, but . . .

Lord A.

Well, then . . .

Tommy

Amersham, it's awfully jolly of you, but—what's the good of ruining a man and—and then telling him not to bother?

Lord A.

Ruining you? Oh—you mean—Bains's, yes. Well,

you see, when I got there—nobody in the hall. Went into the coffee-room. Not a soul. Drawing-room deserted. Went up into card-room. One rubber going on—hard at it. Didn't like to interrupt. Found myself cooling off a bit. Occurred to me : worse things in the world than— (*gesture to card-table*). Many a good fellow . . . Awful temptation, those wide shirt-cuffs . . . Went down and had a whisky and a quiet think. . . . Understand all, forgive all. Damned hypocritical world. Pardons any sin but the sin of being found out. Who was I that I should . . . Tommy, old man (*grips* TOMMY's *hand*). . . . *That's all right.*

TOMMY

I'm—really, I'm——

LORD A.

My only fear is that Enid may . . . you know how difficult it is for a woman not to *talk*. And Enid—between you and me—is the most awful little chatterbox in the British Empire.

> [*At this moment* LADY A.'s *hand appears grasping the top of the screen.* TOMMY *sees it, and, behind* LORD A.'s *back, makes a frantic prohibitive gesture in its direction.*]

However, I know how to frighten her, and I'll undertake to——

> [*The screen falls revealing* LADY A. *in the act of propelling it.* LORD A. *starts and stares round at her. She instantly folds her hands and stands with downcast eyes.*]

LADY A. (*in a low, clear voice*)

Lady Amersham, by all that's wonderful. . . . Lady Amersham by all that's——

LORD A. (*laughing heartily*)

Why, little Enid! I *thought*, when I was on the way, I should find you here. (*Goes to her with outstretched hands.*) My dear child : as if—why, it was a most generous impulse of yours to come and tell our poor Tommy that you—— Just like you! But Lord! what a baby! Running to hide as if . . .

> [LADY A.'s *expression during this speech has gradually changed from blank amazement to horror and from horror to amusement.*]

LADY A. (*faintly*)

Jack! You don't quite . . . I wasn't . . .

LORD A.

You're tired. (*Supports her with one arm.*) No wonder. Hysteria—the curse of the age. Come! Where's your cloak? By the way, I didn't see our car at the door.

LADY A.

No, I told Simpson he needn't——

LORD A.

Quite right. Cold night for man or beast. Blamed myself for keeping my taxi.

> [ROBBINS *meanwhile has furtively produced* LADY A.'s *cloak, and advances to help*

her on with it. LORD A., *reminded of his
existence, returns down stage to* TOMMY.]

LORD A. (*sotto voce*)

That fellow Robertson . . .

TOMMY

Rob*bins.*

LORD A.

There's something about him that. . . . Was it he who
put you up to—— (*gesture to card-table*)

TOMMY

Robbins ? Good heavens ! He's the soul of honour.

LORD A.

Well, it would be just like you to shield him, but (*looks
round and sees his wife standing cloaked. She has moved
away without thanking* ROBBINS, *who stands midway between
her and her husband*) I don't like the look of him.

TOMMY

I assure you . . .

LADY A. (*querulously*)

Jack !

LORD A.

Good-night, dear old fellow. And—I'm *glad* it's
happened. Only—don't do it again, eh ?

193

TOMMY (*dolefully*)

No : 'tisn't a bit of good.

[LORD A. *goes to door followed by* TOMMY.]

ROBBINS (*holding out hand*)

Good-night, Lord Amersham.

LORD A. (*ignoring hand*)

Good-night.

LADY A.

Good-night, Tommy.

TOMMY

Oh, I'm coming down to see you off.

LORD A. (*turning on threshold*)

Dine with us to-morrow.

TOMMY

No, to-morrow, I——

LADY A.

Well, Thursday ?

TOMMY

I should love to, but . . . I'm dining with—with
H. Robbins.

LADY A. and LORD A.

Well, *lunch* on Thursday ?

TOMMY

Lunch ? Y-yes—delighted——

> [TELEPHONE-BELL : ' Trr-trr-trr.' TOMMY
> casts agonised glance at it, wavering
> between it and the AMERSHAMS, as
> he passes out into the hall. ROBBINS sits
> down dejected on a small chair.
>
> TELEPHONE - BELL : ' Trr - trr - trr——
> trrrrrrrrr,' while the CURTAIN falls.]

THE STORY OF THE SMALL BOY AND THE BARLEY-SUGAR

THE STORY OF THE SMALL BOY
AND THE BARLEY-SUGAR

1897.

Little reader, unroll your Map of England.
Look over its coloured counties and find Rutland.
You shall not read this story until you have found Rutland. For
it was there, and in the village of Dauble, that these things happened.
You need not look for Dauble ; it is too small to be marked.

THERE was only one shop in the village, and it was kept by Miss Good, and everybody was very proud of it.

A little further down the street, there was indeed a black, noisy place with flames in it. This was kept by a frightening man who wore a great beard and did not go to the church on Sundays. But I do not think it was a real shop, for only horses went there. The children always ran past it very quickly. But the children never ran past Miss Good's unless they were late for school.

They used to crowd round the window and talk about the red and yellow sweets that were banked up against the panes in a most tempting and delightful fashion. Sometimes one of the boys, greedier than the rest, would stand on tiptoe and press his lips to the glass, declaring he could almost taste the sweets, or ' lollypops,' as he called them. Sometimes Miss Good would come and nod her ringlets to the children, over the bottles of home-made peppermint. How they envied her, living always, as she did, in company so splendid !

A VARIETY OF THINGS

They were not rich, these little children. But most of them were good, and often, when they had been very good, their parents would give them brown pennies. Hardly a day passed but one of them would strut forth from the rest and go solemnly into the shop, soon to return with treasure wrapped in paper. This happy child—were it boy or girl —seldom broke the rather harsh law which ordained that the bag must first of all be handed round among the other children. His or hers were all the sweets that remained. Therefore pear-drops were usually chosen, because they were so small, and half an ounce meant very many pear-drops.

Out of school-hours, Miss Good's window was seldom free from its wistful crowd. Indeed, a certain small boy, named Tommy Tune, was the only one of all the school-children who did not seem to love it. Was he not fond of sweets? He was indeed. Was he never good enough to be given a penny? He was almost always good. But alas! his parents were so poor that they had no pennies to spare for him.

When first he went to the school he used to go and look at the sweet-shop with the other boys and girls, and always took a sweet when it was offered him. But soon he grew ashamed of taking sweets, he who was never able to give any in return. And so he kept away.

If he were ever to have a penny, he was going to buy a stick of barley-sugar and share it with Jill Trellis. She was nine years old, like him; and she had curly brown hair and blue eyes, and he loved her. But she was unkind to him, because he never had a penny. She would not go and play with him in the fields, as he asked her, but preferred to be with the other boys. When Tommy saw her, in the distance, eating their sweets or running races with them or playing at kiss-in-the-ring with them, his cheeks grew very red, and his eyes filled with tears. But somehow he loved her all the more. And he often used to dream of Jill, and of pennies, and of the window that Jill loved.

There were other things than sweets in this window, but they were seldom sold. There were strips of bacon, which were not wanted, because every cottager had a pig. There were bright ribands round reels, but the girls of that village were not vain, and fairs were few. From the low ceiling hung bunches of tallow-candles, that seemed to grow there like fruit, but every one in that village went to bed at sunset. There was starch, but why stiffen linen? And bootlaces, but they always break.

So Miss Good, like a sensible person, had devoted herself to the study of sweets, how to make them cheaply and well, and, as she was fond of little children, she was pleased that they were her chief customers. But it so happened that she herself was also very fond of sweets. She enjoyed tasting them, not only when she wished to see if they were good, but also when she knew quite well that they were good.

Now, one summer's evening, when all the children had gone home to bed, and she was putting up her humble shutters, Miss Good remembered suddenly that it was her birthday. You see, she had not had one for a whole year, and had forgotten that there were such things. She smiled to herself as she bolted the door of her shop, murmuring softly, ' I really must celebrate my birthday.' So she cut down one of the tallow candles and, having lit it, set it upon the counter. ' Illuminations!' she murmured. Then she cast her eye slowly over all the variegated sweets that were in the window. With deft fingers, she selected some of every kind, piling them all, at length, upon the counter. In the fair light of the candle, they sparkled like precious stones.

I am sorry to say that when Miss Good awoke next morning she felt very ill, and regretted not only that it had been her birthday, but also that she had ever been born at all. She felt that she could not serve in the shop that day. And this was serious, for she had no assistant and thus might lose much custom.

Miss Good was at all times, however, a woman of resource. Rising from her bed, she threw open the little lattice-window and called softly for the Queen of the Fairies, with whom, by the way, she was distantly connected. Then she returned to her bed.

In less than a minute, the convolvulus-chariot and team of dragon-flies flew in at the window and drew up sharp on the foot of the bed. Dismissing with a word her escort of butterflies, the tiny Queen alighted on the counterpane and said, ' Miss Good, why did you call for us ? '

The invalid confessed how greedy she had been and implored the Queen not to think ill of her. And Her Majesty, knowing well that the sellers of sweets must ever be exposed to stronger temptations than are ordinary folk, smiled upon her not unkindly.

' Could you possibly,' murmured Miss Good, from her pillow, ' without inconvenience, send a fairy to mind the shop, just for to-day ? '

' On the condition that you never again exceed,' said the Queen.

' I promise,' said Miss Good. ' Thank you very much.

My head aches sadly. I am best alone. Thanks. Remember me kindly to the King.'

With a gracious inclination of her head, the Queen stepped into her chariot and was gone.

Now, as it happened, Tommy Tune's father came home that morning from another village, where for some days he had been making hay. The kind farmer whose hay it was had paid him very handsomely for his work. And when Tommy, having eaten his dinner, took his slate and was starting again for school, his father called him back.

' Tommy son,' he said, ' I have brought back something for you. Shut your eyes and give me your hand.'

Tommy obeyed in wonder. When he opened his eyes and looked to see what was in his hand, he saw—what do you think?—a real, brown penny !

' Oh Father,' he cried, ' how wonderful it is ! And can you really spare it ? '

' I'm not sure that I can,' replied Mr. Tune, rather grimly. ' Run away now before I ask for it back.'

Tommy scampered off.

Far down the road, on the way to school, walked a little girl, whose brown hair curled over her pinafore. It was Jill. Tommy shouted to her to stop and ran still faster. Yesterday he would not have dared to speak to her— certainly not to shout.

When he came nearer, the little girl heard him and looked round. At first, she shook her head and began walking on, but Tommy called to her so eagerly that at length she waited for him.

' Jill ! ' he said to her, shy and breathless. 'Will you come with me after school and buy barley-sugar ? '

' No, I won't,' she said. ' I'm going to play at horses

with Dicky Jones. And what's more, I haven't a penny. And if I had I shouldn't go with you, because I don't like you.'

' But *I* have a penny, Jill,' he pleaded.

' Show it ! ' rejoined the little girl.

Tommy showed it.

' Well,' she said, after a while, ' I won't play at horses to-day. And I—I think you're much nicer than Dicky Jones. And—and—oh Tommy ! why are you always so unkind to me now ? '

Tommy hung his head.

When they came to the school, the school bell had almost ceased tolling, and all the children had gone in. Just outside the porch, Jill whispered, ' Tommy, I'm not angry with you. Kiss me! Quickly ! '

How very slowly the time went for Tommy that afternoon ! He could only just see the top of Jill's curly head. She always sat far away from him, for, though she was a girl, she was cleverer than he, and was in a higher class. But he thought about her all the time. The big round figures seemed to write themselves on his slate, he knew not how. Whenever a ' nought ' came, he put four little dots in it, two for Jill's eyes, one for her nose, one for her mouth. And all his sums came out right, that afternoon, long before the other boys and girls had done theirs. Then there was nothing for him to do but to keep his eyes on the clock. Thirty whole minutes more ! What was thirty times sixty ?

He remembered that Jill's class did their spelling-lesson in the last half-hour. Jill would stand up with the rest by the Teacher's desk. Perhaps she would look round at him. He could scarcely believe that soon they would be sitting together, all alone in the field, with a stick of barley-sugar.

When Jill went up with the others to the high desk, she did look round at Tommy, with her finger to her lips, just where he had kissed her. In another instant she had clasped her hands behind her and was looking up at the Teacher.

She was near the top of her class, and her turn came soon. She was given a very easy word to spell; but she must have been thinking of other things, I am afraid, for she failed in the given word : she spelt Cow with an U. Tommy, in his corner, blushed scarlet.

When her turn came round again, she spelt KITE with a C. The Teacher, who had always thought her to be one of the best of her pupils, frowned. 'Be careful, Jill Trellis!' she said sharply. Tommy held his slate very tightly with both hands.

Jill was told to spell Box. 'B,' she said, 'o,'—and she stopped short.

'Be very careful,' said the Teacher. 'You cannot be attending. B, o,—well ? '

Jill shook her head.

'x,' said the Teacher, 'you very abominable little girl ! Fetch the Dunce's Cap and stand on the stool. You will stay here for an hour after school is over and learn two pages of hard words.'

So Jill fetched the Dunce's Cap and climbed up on to the stool and clasped her hands behind her.

Nor did she look at Tommy when the clock struck four and the school-children trooped out.

For some time Tommy stood in the porch. There, at least, he was near his poor sweetheart. He would wait there till she was set free.

But, as the minutes went by, he grew more and more miserable. He could not bear to think of her in there with her spelling-book. He would run away somewhere and be at the gate to meet her when she came out.

As he ran, it struck him that she might be comforted if he met her with the barley-sugar in his hand. And so he stopped at the door of Miss Good's shop and walked boldly in.

To his surprise, Miss Good, whose ringlets he had often seen through the window, was not there, and in her stead, smiling from behind the counter, was a beautiful young person with bright yellow hair and blue wings.

'Good afternoon, little Sir,' said this young person. 'What may I serve you with?'

'A penny stick of barley-sugar,' said Tommy. He spoke in rather a surly voice, for he did not like any one to be pretty except Jill; though Jill, of course, was much prettier than this stranger, in his opinion.

'What a pleasant afternoon, is it not?' said the young person, taking from a glass bottle a short, twisted stick of barley-sugar.

Tommy stretched out his hand in silence.

'Quite seasonable!' she continued, looking down at her little customer and holding the stick just beyond his reach. 'But you are behaving as if it were mid-winter, and the ground were white with snow, and the sky black with it. I suppose you are what would be called unhappy.'

'Yes I am,' said Tommy sulkily, 'and I want the barley-sugar.'

'Certainly, little Sir, I will not detain you.' Lightly she blew upon the yellow stick. 'Now, understand that every time you take a bite at that, you can wish, and all

206

your wishes will come true. Say " Thank you " and give me your penny.'

Tommy opened his eyes very wide and thanked her.

' Good afternoon,' she said, dropping his penny into the till.

Tommy ran, as hard as he could, to a certain field. He held the barley-sugar tightly in his hand. He knew what he was going to wish for first. His eyes sparkled as he ran. Visions of what he would wish for later on floated vaguely in his mind—a lovely garden of vegetables for his mother, a lovely farm for his father, for himself a regiment of wooden soldiers, taller than he was. But these fair visions he hardly heeded. He was thinking only of his first wish.

That he might get more quickly into the field, he climbed through a break in the hedge, caring not how the brambles scratched him, and jumped over the ditch on to the grass beyond. There, after his run, flushed and trembling with excitement, he put the yellow stick to his lips. He set his teeth upon the very edge of it, so as not to take more than a tiny bite. Then, shutting his eyes tight, he said aloud, ' I wish Jill to come here at once.'

And, when he looked, there stood Jill before him, in her Dunce's Cap. In her hand she held a spelling-book, and her eyes were full of tears. But Tommy flung his arms round her neck, so quickly that the book and the cap both fell to the ground. Tommy kissed away all her tears.

' Leave go, Tommy ! ' she cried at last. ' Tell me why I am here. Why am I in this field ? ' she asked, staring around.

' I wished for you to come, Jill,' the boy answered.

' But I was in the school-room. Why am I in the field ? '

' This is a stick of barley-sugar,' Tommy began.

' So it is,' said Jill, drawing nearer. ' It looks good.'

' But it isn't like the others,' Tommy went on ; ' because, you see, a fairy gave it me for my penny ; and when you take a bite, you wish ; and your wish comes true. I wished for you, Jill. And I'm going to wish for—oh ! heaps of things. You shall wish too.'

Swiftly she snatched the yellow stick from his hand and ran away, crushing it all into her mouth at once.

' Jill ! Jill ! ' cried the boy piteously as he chased her round the field. ' Do leave a little ! '

At last he caught her and held her fast in his arms. ' Haven't you left a little ? ' he asked her.

She shook her head from side to side. Her mouth was too full for speech.

' And Jill !—you never wished ! ' he said sadly.

' Oh yes, I did,' she answered presently. ' I wished you hadn't eaten that first bit.'

Little reader, roll up your Map of England.

But first look once more at Rutland, that you may remember where it is.

Perhaps you have often laughed at Rutland, because it is the tiniest of all the counties and is painted pink.

Now see how neatly and well they have painted it, never going over the edges, as you would have done.

And know, also, that though it looks so small, it is really more than three times as big as your nursery, and that things can happen there.

It is very foolish to laugh at Rutland.

YAI AND THE MOON

YAI AND THE MOON

1897.

THE Bay of Yedo is all blue and yellow. The village of
Haokami is pink. And Umanosuké, who ruled the village
worthily, was a widower. And Yai, his daughter, was
wayward.

The death of his wife had grieved Umanosuké. ' She
was more dear to me,' he had cried over her tomb, ' than
the plum-tree in my garden, more dear than the half of all
my pied chrysanthemums. And now she is dead. The
jewelled honeycomb is taken from me. Void is the pavilion
of my desire. As an untrod island, as a little island in a
sea of tears, so am I. My wife is dead. What is left to
me ? ' Yai, not more then than a baby, had sidled up to
him, cooing, ' I, father ! ' And the villagers had murmured
in lowly unison, ' We, great sir ! ' And so the widower had
straightway put from him his hempen weeds and all the
thistles of his despair, had lifted his laughing child upon
his shoulder, and touched with his hand the bowed heads
of the villagers, saying, ' Bliss, of all things most wonderful,
is fled from me. But Authority remains, and therefore will
I make no more lamentation.'

Henceforth Umanosuké lived for Authority. Full of
wisdom were his precepts, and of necessity his decrees.
Whenever the villagers quarrelled, as villagers will, among
themselves, and struck one another with their paper-fans
and parasols, at his coming they would lie flat upon the

green ground, eager for his arbitrage. With the villagers he had not any trouble. With Yai, alas ! he had.

' Five years are gone,' he said sternly to her, one morning, ' since the sun glanced upon that sugared waterfall, your mother. Nor ever once have you sought to please me, since the day when you delivered yourself into my charge. The toys that I fashioned for your pleasure you have not heeded, and from the little pictures that I painted for your good you have idly turned your eyes. When I would awe you to obedience, you do but flout me. When I make myself even as a child and would be your playmate, you drive me from your presence. You will soon be eight years old. Behave, I beseech you, better ! '

Yai ran into the garden, laughing.

On the morning of her thirteenth birthday, Umanosuké resumed his warning. ' Ten years ago,' he said, ' there flew from me the shining heron's wing that was your mother. I would she were here that she might assuage the bitter sorrow you are always to me. You break the figured tablets from which I would teach you wisdom. Strewn with unfingered dust are the books you should have long learnt utterly. Your feet fly always over the sand or through the flowers and feather-grasses. I see you from my window bend your attentive ear to the vain music of the seashell. I often hear you in foolish parley with the birds. Me, your father, you do dishonour. Reflect ! You are growing old. You will never see twelve again. Behave, I beseech you, better ! '

Yai ran into the garden, pouting.

On the morning of the day before her wedding-day, Umanosuké called her to him and said, once and for all, ' Since faded and fell that fair treillage of convolvulus, than which I can find no better simile for your mother, it is already fifteen round years. And lo ! in nothing but dreams and truancy have you spent your girlhood. I, who begat you, have grown sad in contemplating all your faults. Had I not, knowing the wisdom of the philosophers, believed that in the span of every life there is good and evil equally distributed, and that your evil girlhood was surely the preamble of a most perfect prime, your faults had been intolerable. But I was comforted in my belief, and when I betrothed you to young Sanza, the son of Oiyâro, my heart was filled with fair hopes. Only illusions !'

'But, father,' said Yai, 'I do not love Sanza.'

'How can you tell that you do not love him,' her father demanded, 'seeing that you hardly know him?'

'He is ugly, father,' said Yai. 'He wears strange garments. His voice is harsh. Twice we have walked together by the side of the sea, and when he praised my beauty and talked of all he had learned at the university, and of all he wished me to learn also, I knew that I did not love him. His thoughts are not like mine.'

'That may well be,' Umanosuké answered, 'seeing that he was held to be the finest student of his year, and that you are more ignorant than a hare. As for his face, it is topped with the highest forehead in Haokami. As for his garments, they are symbols of advancement. In fourteen languages he can lift his voice. I am an old man now, a man of the former fashion, and many of Sanza's thoughts seem strange to me, as to you. But when I am in his presence I bow humbly before his intellect. He is a marvellous young man, indeed. He understands all things. If you mean that you are unworthy of him, I certainly agree.'

'Then, it is that I am unworthy of him, father,' faltered Yai, with downcast eyes.

'Sanza does not think so,' said her father, more gently. 'He told me yesterday that he thought you were quite worthy of him. And as I look at you, little daughter, and see how fair a maid you are, I think he was right. It is because I love you that I would you were without fault. I have never been able to rule you. It is therefore that I give you gladly to Sanza, who will understand you, as he understands all other things.'

'Perhaps,' said Yai, 'Sanza is too wise to understand me, and I am not wise enough to love him. I do not know how it is—but oh, father! indulge me in one whim, and I will never be graceless nor unfilial again! Tell Sanza you will not let him be my bridegroom!'

'To-morrow you will be his wife,' said Umanosuké. 'That you think yourself indifferent to him, is nothing to me. You are betrothed to him. He has given to you, in due form, a robe of silken tissue, a robe incomparably broidered with moons and lilac. When once the lover has given to the maiden the robe of silken tissue, his betrothal is sacred in the eyes of our God.'

'Father,' said Yai, 'the robe has been given to me indeed. It lies in my room, and over all its tissue are moons and lilac. But lilac is said to be the flower of unfaith, and moons are but images of him whom I love. Ever since I was little, I have loved the Moon. As a little child I loved him, and now my heart is not childish, but I love him still. From my window, father, I watch him as he rises in silver from the edge of the sea. I watch him as he climbs up the hollow sky. For love of him I forgo sleep, and when he sinks into the sea he leaves me desolate. Of no man but him can I be the bride.'

Umanosuké raised his hand. 'The Moon,' he said, 'is
the sacred lantern that our God has given us. We must
not think of it but as of a lantern. I do not know the
meaning of your thoughts. There is mischief in them and
impiety. I pray you, put them from you, lest they fall as
a curse upon your nuptials. I did but send for you that
I might counsel you to bear yourself this afternoon, in
Sanza's presence, as a bride should, with deference and
love, not with unmaidenly aversion. It is not well that
the bridegroom, when he comes duly on the eve of his
wedding to kiss the hand of his bride, and to sprinkle her
chamber with rose-leaves, should be treated ungraciously
and put to shame. Little daughter, I will not argue with
you. Know only that this wedding is well devised for
your happiness. If you love me but a little, try to please
me with obedience. I am older than you, and I know more.
Behave, I beseech you, better !'

Yai ran into the garden, weeping.

She paced up and down the long path of porcelain. She
beat her hands against the bark of her father's favourite
uce-tree, whose branches were always spangled with
fandangles, and cursed the name of her bridegroom. For
hours she wandered among the flower-beds, calling upon
the name of her love.

The gardeners watched her furtively from their work,
and murmured, smiling one to another, ' This evening we
need not carry forth our water-jars, for Yai has watered
all the flowers with her tears.'

When the hour came for her bridegroom's visit, Yai had
bathed her eyes in orange-water, and sat waiting at her

window. She saw him, a tiny puppet in the far distance, start from the pavilion that was his home. As he came nearer, she noted his brisk tread, and how the sun shone on his tall black European hat. What a complacent smile curved his lips ! How foolish he looked, for all his learning ! In one hand he swung a black umbrella, in the other a small parcel of brown paper. 'He will release me,' whispered Yai ; but her heart misgave her, and she shrank away from the window.

When her nurse ushered Sanza into the room, Yai hardly turned her head.

'Well,' he said cheerily, as he placed his hat on the floor, ' here I am, you see ! Quite punctual, I think ? Brought my rose-leaves along with me. Really, my dear Yai,' he said, after a pause, ' I do think you might rise to meet me when I come into the room. You know I don't stickle for sentiment—far from it—but surely, on such an occasion, a little display of affection wouldn't be amiss. Personally, you know, I object to all this rose-leaf business ; but I'm not going to offend your father's religious views, and it's really rather a quaint old ceremony in its way ; and I *do* think that you might—what shall I say ?—meet me half-way.'

Yai came forward listlessly.

' You'll excuse the suggestion,' he laughed, shaking her hand. ' Now, I had better undo my parcel, I suppose ? I expect you know more about these little Japanese customs than I do ; ' and he began to loosen the string.

' What have you in there ? ' asked Yai.

' Why, the rose-leaves, to be sure ! ' Sanza replied, producing a tin that had once held cocoa.

' Most lovers bring their rose-leaves in a bowl, I fancy,'

said Yai, with a faint smile. 'But it is no matter. Please do not sprinkle them yet.'

'How stupid of me!' exclaimed Sanza, throwing back his handful of rose-leaves into the tin. 'If one does a thing at all, let it be done correctly. I have to kiss your hand first, of course.'

'Please do not kiss my hand, Sanza,' the girl said simply. 'I do not love you. I do not wish to be your bride.'

Sanza whistled.

'What about that silk material I sent you the other day?' he asked sharply. 'I understood that your failure to return it was *ipso facto* an acceptance of my proposal?'

'I kept the silken robe that was broidered with moons and lilac,' Yai murmured, 'because I wished to please my father, whom I have often grieved. I thought then that I could be your bride. Now I know that I cannot.'

'Why this change of front?' gasped her lover.

'I have no good reason,' she said, 'that I can give you; only that I thought I was stronger than I am—stronger than my love.'

'If you'll excuse me,' muttered Sanza, with momentary irrelevance, 'I'll sit down.' And he squatted upon the floor, disposing the tails of his frock-coat around him. 'May I ask,' he said at length, 'to what love you refer?'

'My love for the Moon,' Yai answered.

'The—the *what*?' gasped Sanza.

'The Moon,' she repeated, adding rather foolishly, 'I —I thought perhaps you had guessed.'

Sanza laughed heartily.

'Well, really,' he said, 'you quite took me in. I should suggest your becoming an actress, if it weren't for native prejudices. You'ld go far. Oh, very good! Ha, ha!'

'I am not jesting, Sanza,' said Yai sadly. 'I am very earnest. Ever since I was little, I have loved the Moon. As a little child I loved him, and now my heart is not childish, but I love him still. My heart grows glad as he rises in silver from the edge of the sea and climbs up the hollow sky. When he climbs quickly, I shudder lest he fall; when he lingers, I try to fancy it is for love of me; when he sinks at length into the sea, I weep bitterly.'

Sanza began to humour her.

'Oh yes,' he said, 'the Moon's a wonderful climber. I've noticed that. And a very good fellow, too, from all accounts. I don't happen to know him personally. He was senior to me at the university. I must get you to introduce us.'

'You jest poorly,' said Yai.

Sanza frowned.

'Come, come,' he resumed presently, 'you know as well as I do that the Moon is just an extinct planet, 237,000 miles distant from the earth. Perhaps you didn't know? Well, selenography is rather a hobby of mine, and I'll give you one or two little facts. The Moon is a subject which has attracted a great many physiographists in all ages. Thanks to the invention of photography, we moderns have accumulated a considerable amount of knowledge regarding it. The negatives obtained at the Lick Observatory, for example, prove conclusively that the immense craters and mountainous ridges visible upon its surface, so far from being surrounded with an atmosphere similar in density to our own, are, in fact, enclosed only by a gaseous envelope, not less than 200 times thinner than the most rarefied atmosphere obtainable on the earth.'

But Yai had shut her ears.

'Sanza,' she said, when he ceased, 'will you release me? If you think me mad, you cannot wish me to be your bride.'

For a moment Sanza hesitated—only for a moment.

'Madness,' he said, 'is a question of degree. We are all potentially mad. If you were left to indulge in these absurd notions, you would certainly become mad, in time. As it is, I fancy you have a touch of Neuromania. And when you speak I have noticed a slight tendency to Echolalia. But these are trifles, my dear. Any sudden change of life is apt to dispel far more serious symptoms. Your very defects, small though they are, will make me all the more watchful and tender towards you when I am your husband.'

'You are very cruel and very cowardly,' sobbed Yai, 'and I hate you!'

'Nonsense!' said Sanza, snatching one of her hands and kissing it loudly.

In another minute the room had been sprinkled with rose-leaves, and Yai was alone.

At sunset her father came to the room and bent over her and kissed her. 'Do not weep, little daughter,' he said. 'It is well that you should be wed, though you are so unwilling. Sleep happily now, little daughter. To-morrow, all in your honour, the way will be strewn with anemones and golden grain. Little lanterns will waver in the almond trees.'

Yai spoke not a word.

But when her father had reached the threshold of her room, she ran swiftly to him and flung her arms around his neck, and whispered to him through tears, 'Forgive me for being always an evil daughter.'

Umanosuké caressed her and spoke gentle words. And when presently he left her he barred the door of her room. For in that land there is an old custom, which ordains that the bride's room be sealed on the wedding-eve, lest the bride be stolen away in the night.

Umanosuké's footsteps grew faint in the distance. So soon as she could hear them no more, Yai shook the door, noiselessly, if peradventure it were not rightly barred. It did not yield. Noiselessly she crept across the floor, the rose-leaves brushing her bare and tiny feet. Noiselessly she slid back the wooden grill from her window. She wrapped her skirt very tightly round her, and raised herself on to the ledge. Down a trellis that covered the outer wall she climbed lightly. No one saw her.

Darting swiftly from shadow to shadow, she passed down the long garden, and dragged from its shed the little reeded skiff that her father had once given to her. She did not dare drag it down the beach, lest the noise of the rustling shingle should betray her. Easily (for it was light as a toy) she lifted it on her shoulder, and carried it down, so, to the darkening waters, launched it, and stepped in.

She knew at what point on the edge of the great sea her lover would rise. She knew by the aspect of the stars that he would rise before the end of another hour. Could she reach the edge of the great sea so soon? Crouching low in the skiff, a little figure scrupulously balanced, she brushed the water with her paddle. Strong and supple was her wrist, and sure were her eyes, and swiftly the frail craft sped on over the waters. Never once did the maid flag nor falter, though her hands grew cold and stiff in their exertion. Though darkness closed in around her, and the waters rushed past her, on either side, with a shrill sound as of weeping, she had no fear, but only love in her heart. Gazing steadfastly before her at that glimmering white line where the sky curves down upon the sea, and ever whispering through her lips the name of her love, she held her swift course over the waters.

Clearer, clearer to her gaze grew the white line and the arched purple that rested on it. Another minute, and she could hear the waves lapping its surface, a sweet monotony of music, seeming to call her on. A few more strokes of her paddle, swept with a final impulse, and the boat bore her with a yet swifter speed. Soon she suffered it to glide on obliquely, till it grazed the white line with its prow. She had reached the tryst of her devotion. Faint and quivering, she lay back and waited there.

After a while, she leant over the side of the boat and peered down into the sea. Far, far under the surface she seemed to descry a little patch of silver, of silver that was moving. She clasped her hands to her eyes and gazed down again. The silver was spreading, wider and wider, under the water, till the water's surface became even as a carpet of dazzling silver.

The Moon rose through the sea, and paused under the canopy of the sky.

So great, so fair was he, of countenance so illustrious, that little Yai did but hide her head in the folds of her garment, daring not to look up at him.

She heard a voice, that was softer and more melancholy than the west wind, saying to her, ' Child of the ruler of Haokami, why sought you to waylay me ? ' And again the voice said, ' Why sought you to waylay me ? '

' Because,' Yai answered faintly, ' because I have long loved you.'

And as she crouched before him, the Moon covered her with silver, insomuch that she was able to look up into his eyes, being herself radiant, even as he was. And she stretched out her arms to him and besought him that she might sail over the sky with him that night.

' Nay,' said the Moon, ' but you know not what you ask. Over the sky you might sail in my embrace, and love me, and be my darling. I would bear you among the stars and be with you in the shadows of the clouds. The tiny world would lie outspread beneath us. In the wonder of our joy we would not heed it. We would mingle the cold silver of our lips, and in the wreath of our arms our love-dreams would come true. But soon, so soon, I should sink into the sea yonder. On the grey surface of the sea I should leave you to drown.'

' Take me in your arms ! ' cried the girl.

And the Moon bent down to her and took her gently in his arms.

Next morning, the Sun, as he was rising from the sea, saw a little pale body floating over the waves.

' Why ! ' he exclaimed, ' there is the child of the ruler of Haokami. She was always wayward. I knew she would come to a bad end. And this was to have been her wedding-day too ! I suppose she was really in love with me and swam to meet me. How very sad ! ' And he covered her with gold.

' After all,' he muttered, rising a little higher, ' it does not do for these human beings to have ideas above their station. It always leads to unhappiness. The dead child down there would soon have forgotten her unfortunate attachment to me, if she had only stayed ashore and married that impertinent little fellow, who is always spying at me through his confounded telescope. And there he is, to be sure ! up betimes and strutting about his garden, with a fine new suit on ! Quite the bridegroom ! '